C000179792

SMALL ROBOTS

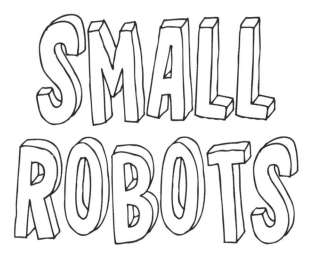

SMALL ROBOTS

THOMAS HEASMAN-HUNT

unbound

First published in 2019

Unbound
6th Floor Mutual House, 70 Conduit Street, London W1S 2GF
www.unbound.com

Text Design by PDQ Digital Media Solutions Ltd.

A CIP record for this book is available from the British Library

ISBN 978-1-78352-822-6 (hbk)
ISBN 978-1-78352-823-3 (ebook)

Printed in Slovenia by DZS Grafik

1 3 5 7 9 8 6 4 2

For Emma, of course,
and for the rest of the Small Robots family who have supported
this project both materially and otherwise

The Three Laws of Small Robotics

1. Be kind
2. Be helpful
3. Do your best

Introduction

Small Robots is a project which started life on Twitter, with an account called @smolrobots. The stated purpose of this account was, simply, to post amusing pictures of diminutive, cute automatons that would do various helpful things. I drew the pictures and wrote the words and I hoped it would make people smile. It ended up doing a lot more: by including robots that addressed more existential problems than the successful retrieval of tea or items from high shelves, Small Robots struck a chord and swiftly grew in popularity – a journey that has culminated with the book you're holding right now!

Although Teabot was the first Small Robot drawn and posted, the genesis of the concept came a little earlier on the same day. My wife, Emma, is a healthcare scientist working in a hospital lab. One chilly November morning she sent me a fairly innocuous email about one of the machines she uses refusing to work because it was too cold. She suggested she might knit it a jumper. Inspired by this image, I opened up Microsoft Paint on my computer and produced a crude sketch of a blocky robot on tracks wrapped in a woolly jumper, which I sent to her. This so amused us that I pondered creating a Twitter account to post similar sorts of pictures, albeit of higher quality. Her response to my suggestion was simply, 'Yes. Yes, you should.' So I did.

Since that fateful day, Small Robots has grown and grown (while still remaining small – or at least smol) and touched the lives of people from all over the world who have, in turn, given incredibly kind feedback, created fanart and even brought some robots to life in the form of knitted or crocheted characters or 3D printed figurines. Frankly, it's all a bit weird. Thank you to everyone who has been part of this bizarre adventure, who has sent suggestions, provided support – not least the funding of this book – and spread the word.

Every illustration featured here and on the account is drawn by hand, by me, albeit now using a digital stylus and tablet, with no additional tweaking with image-editing software. It's therefore been a labour of love for almost a year now, and has seen me through some particularly difficult personal situations and a very strange geopolitical environment. I've always been frank about addressing wider problems using Small Robots, and the response to that has been really gratifying. People sometimes mistake the account for a place of pure positivity, but that's not precisely right; not everyone has the luxury of being able to opt out of the problems facing society, and Small Robots is dedicated to providing a welcoming space for people from marginalised communities, which is why some of the sections in this book are focused on those kinds of robots.

Of course, I couldn't include every single Small Robot that I've drawn in this publication. I and my publishers settled on one hundred as a nice, representative number and I've tried to curate a wide selection of some of the more popular robots along with some personal favourites. If you've enjoyed reading about these, there are many more to discover online!

Thomas Heasman-Hunt, November 2019

HANDYBOTS

Perhaps the most basic broad category of Small Robots are the ones I've dubbed 'Handybots'. All Small Robots are handy, in a sense (well, mostly…), but the idea of the Handybots is that their purpose is something fairly mundane and fundamentally practical. Of all the Small Robots, these are the ones most likely to have functions that could be outsourced to a suitable mundane solution, like a pamphlet that tells you when your bins are collected, or a larger cupboard. But do those things have cute little faces on them? No, they do not.

A common response to many of the robots I draw is a question that generally begins with the phrase, 'Can this robot also…' The answer is no. However that sentence ends, it's no. You see, the whole point of a Small Robot is that it has a single function that it pursues to the exclusion of all else. There are two reasons for this: 1) it's funnier and 2) it leaves more creative space for additional robots. I could have just drawn a Butlerbot or something that does anything you want, but where's the fun in that? Indeed, most actual roboticists and engineers would see a machine that can fulfil a variety of disparate functions as not only desirable, but in a sense more practical. A robot that can lift things can lift anything, after all. Designing a robot to only lift a particular item is positively perverse. Well, I'm not a roboticist or an engineer. In fact, I don't know anything about robots. Small Robots only do one thing. Deal with it.

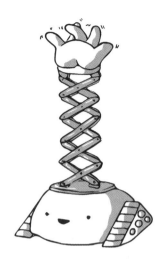

REACHBOT

Primary Function:
Reachbot is a Small Robot for getting things off shelves if you're a person who is also small.

Notable Features:
All-terrain track assembly, extendable reaching arm, wiggly fingers.

Dimensions:
Variable, depending on how extended its arm is.

Reachbot provides benefits for two distinct markets: first, and primarily, for small people who may not be able to reach things. Secondly, for very tall people who are often asked to reach things by small people. But whoever's using it, Reachbot's job is the same: to reach for things. That's why we called it that. Just point to what you need and Reachbot will motor into position and then deploy its big hand to get the item. No longer will you need to risk climbing a ladder, balancing on a stool or throwing another, less valuable possession at the thing you want in the faint hope of knocking it off its perch.

Sadly, there is an unanticipated design flaw with Reachbot: because its eyes are on its body, it can't actually see what it's reaching for.

TAPEBOT

Primary Function:
Tapebot helps you find the end of the roll of sticky tape.

Notable Features:
Hyper-sensitive finger texture, retractable nails, so many arms.

Dimensions:
About the same size as a roll of tape.

We're sorry, but life is much too short for messing about with sticky tape. You could just never give anyone any presents, or let your handmade posters and signs battle gravity by themselves for once, but a much better solution is to take advantage of Tapebot's skills. With a little flourish, it flicks up the roll of tape and twirls it in its multitude of arms, locating the end, picking it free and passing it back to you ready to pull free to administer a semi-transparent adhesive strip for whatever purpose you require. Maybe repairing a beloved artistic effort by a well-meaning but untalented child, or doing a weird impression of a pig. Whatever. It's your life.

Don't ask it to actually use the tape though. It's not for that.

Of course, you could just use a tape dispenser to… oh.

PARCELBOT

Primary Function:
Parcelbot waits on your doorstep when you're expecting a parcel that won't fit through the letterbox and looks after it for you until you get home.

Notable Features:
High boredom threshold, not unduly bothered by rain, signature duplication function, small repertoire of delivery-related small talk.

Dimensions:
Sufficient arm span to grasp even fairly large parcels.

Online ordering has revolutionised the way we shop, eliminating the need for a person to venture out into the world and interact with other humans, instead simply having their consumer goods delivered straight to their home at the click of a button. In practice though, this convenience is mitigated by the final link in the chain between website and your front door – the delivery service. It's not their fault: the infrastructure just wasn't designed for this volume and size of parcels! People just used to send flimsy little letters! So now, to avoid having to go to the *shop*, you have to wait for the weekend to go to the *depot* instead. You can see where this is going: Parcelbot loiters around outside your door and, when the postman arrives, it takes possession of the parcel for you. Job done, worries over, Christmas saved.

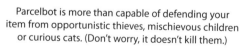

Parcelbot is more than capable of defending your item from opportunistic thieves, mischievous children or curious cats. (Don't worry, it doesn't kill them.)

Parcelbots can also be registered and issued with a special ID card that allows them to sign for parcels in your absence.

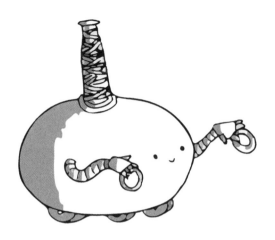

BANDBOT

Primary Function:
Bandbot fashions and distributes an endless supply of precious, precious hairbands.

Notable Features:
Extendable arms, internal hairband-weaving manufactory, retractable deployment cone.

Dimensions:
Not big enough to overstretch the hairbands.

If you're a person who has long hair and sometimes, often or always ties it back to stop it getting in your eyes or mouth, you'll understand the scourge of the missing hairband. These creations, despite possessing the apparent ontological inertia of any physical object in the universe, have a heretofore unknown ability to simply vanish from existence. Do they shift into some higher spatial dimension, like the opposite of a Möbius strip? Do they disintegrate via exposure to human hair? Are they coveted by some race of supernatural or extra-terrestrial being? No one knows, but Bandbot is here with the solution: inexhaustible hairbands that it makes itself and then gives to you. It harvests the material for its ceaseless industry by recycling clothes fibres it finds in plentiful supply in the average suburban carpet.

No hairbands? Why don't you check your other pocket? He he.

The deployment cone slides neatly into Bandbot's hull and emerges a short time later replete with its bounty of fresh head accoutrements.

PLANTBOT

Primary Function:
Plantbot waters your plants for you when you're away from home.

Notable Features:
Capacious interior, 3D tilt function for achieving full sprinkle coverage, comprehensive horticultural database with auto-update facility, mysterious ability to work taps.

Dimensions:
One watering can.

If pets are tricky to take on holiday with you, plants are even worse. Just try getting a load of native flora through foreign customs, let alone finding space in the average hotel resort to plant your marigolds in an environment that will allow them to thrive. Arid Mediterranean soil? Get real! No, a much better idea is to leave Plantbot in charge of the garden while you aren't home. It'll do the rounds as often as needed, making sure everything is nicely watered. It doesn't do any other kind of care for your plants, so if you're looking to win awards or grow something really fussy, maybe make other arrangements. Frankly, if you're a professional you shouldn't really be leaving things in the hands of a robot, particularly one that doesn't have any.

Don't waste its time with this kind of nonsense either.

Plantbot isn't really optimised for scaling ladders, but it has quite a good knack for improvising solutions if needs be.

BINSBOT

Primary Function:
Binsbot knows what day the bins go out after a Bank Holiday.

Notable Features:
Multidimensional computational matrix, triple backup processing core, piece of chalk.

Dimensions:
Smaller than you might think (because much of its processing
architecture exists in a higher spatial dimension).

Perhaps the most sophisticated of all the Small Robots, Binsbot is so intelligent it almost qualifies as fully sapient. Thankfully, all of its vast intellect is bent towards its single, unending task: to calculate when the bins go out after a Bank Holiday. What arcane mathematics it employs in this endeavour are beyond the ken of all but the seven most intelligent people on Earth, and even they would need to devote every spare neurone to such a project and would probably starve to death in the process. It's no wonder Binsbots are so coveted, and the resulting Robot Riots that occurred shortly after it was first put on sale led to all of the units being taken into public ownership so that they could benefit all mankind instead of being a source of strife. To this day, some suspect that Binsbot might be the catalyst of the feared 'robot uprising' that robosceptics claim is inevitable, but like all Small Robots, they have proved entirely benevolent. We salute you, Binsbot, master of time and space.

Unlike most Small Robots, Binsbot is of sufficient sophistication to manage two jobs. When not worrying about bins, it's employed to tune up supercomputers.

GUESTSHOWERBOT

Primary Function:
Carry Guestshowerbot in your washbag when you stay at someone's house
and let it figure out their bizarre shower controls before you manage
to drown yourself or burn half your skin off or something.

Notable Features:
Top-mounted water-repellent veined awning, moisture-resistant lower-ambulator coverings,
pre-loaded with PDF instruction manuals for most modern shower models, literally magic.

Dimensions:
Fits nicely on the soap-holder bit.

What is it with showers? *Kettles* all work the same way. *Irons* all work the same way. No one gets confused trying to open the *fridge* in a stranger's house. But apparently showers are fair game for appliance manufacturers to really stretch their creative muscles and design a user interface so uniquely obtuse that an inexperienced operator can risk actual bodily harm every time they dare to activate the thing. Well, we've had enough, and we've designed Guestshowerbot to deal with the problem. It can puzzle its way through any shower, no matter how weird, so you can avoid becoming an amusing anecdote the next time someone comes over.

Worked it out!

Before going into battle, Guestshowerbot dons its gear. Wait… why did we make them separate components anyway?

BALLOONBOT

Primary Function:
Balloonbot deflates unwanted balloons so they don't burst near your face and frighten you.

Notable Features:
Capacious interior, conical exhaust port, spoked wheels for some reason.

Dimensions:
Sufficient volume to hold the contents of six average-sized balloons.

Balloons are a source of joy for children and adults alike – colourful spheroid air-prisons that liven up even the dullest party with their gentle undulations. However, for some benighted individuals, a balloon is a source of terror! It's easy to be lulled into a false sense of security by their vibrant buoyancy, but one false move and BANG! For those who dread the sight of the latex orbs at a gathering, Balloonbot is the solution. It bravely scouts ahead of you, ensuring any balloons are safely deflated before you reach the vicinity. Some call it a party pooper, but better a pooper than a popper.

Balloonbot's courage is boundless; it hurls itself towards its targets with near-reckless determination.

WRAPBOT

Primary Function:
Wrapbot wraps all your presents for you.

Notable Features:
Multiple processors for seamless multitasking, advanced spatial-modelling software, handwriting duplication function, direct wireless connection to Tapebot.

Dimensions:
Large enough to do your big present.

Ugh, *wrapping*. Some people are good at it, some people are bad at it, but everyone hates it. Why do we subject ourselves to this torment? What do any of us get out of the bizarre practice of keeping the nature of a gift secret until an arbitrary date? It just makes litter, and you don't want Litterbot shoving a load of tape and wrapping paper down your windpipe on Christmas morning. Anyway, here's Wrapbot, who can't get enough of pointlessly dressing up presents. It has six segments for simultaneous wrapping of several presents and, despite its bidigital hands, is pretty dextrous. Just let it do its thing and your celebration will have all the ripped-paper-generating fun of your childhood memories.

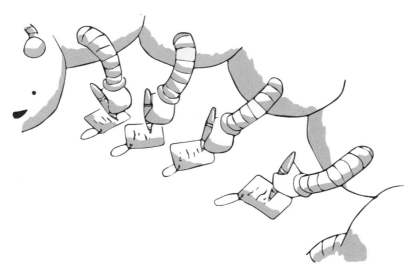

And it's also pretty good for doing the labels! It even imitates your handwriting, so no one will know you don't actually care about them.

STORAGEBOT

Primary Function:
Look after your precious things with Storagebot, whose gullet is an interdimensional aperture to a pocket universe that is pleasingly roomy. Just administer a slight tickle to retrieve a possession.

Notable Features:
Interdimensional gateway, full (if erratic) inventory feature,
lockable face, adorable chubby cheeks.

Dimensions:
Uh… pass.

No one has enough storage, but with Storagebot you'll have more than you can ever use – a whole universe of it! Okay, it's a relatively small universe and there isn't a lot in it at first, but it's still pretty handy to have. Just get Storagebot to open wide and dump whatever you want inside for safekeeping. As Storagebot fills up, it does start to show some effects, bulging and waddling, but this is mostly a user-interface feature so you know how much room is left. You're probably wondering how we made Storagebot. Where did the universe come from? How did we burrow through the skein of space-time separating it from our own universe to create the aperture? Is putting it inside a little robot really the best idea? These are all excellent questions to which there are equally excellent answers, but sadly space precludes us from going into further detail in this publication.

Just a normal interdimensional aperture that spans the conceptual n-space barrier between non-contiguous space-time hyper-volumes.

BLEURGH!

FOODBOTS

Teabot
Cakebot
Dairybot
Dunkbot
Menubot
Brewbot
Chocbot

Coffeebot
Coldbot
Onionbot
Beerbot
Winebot
Rollingpinbot
Recipebot

Aren't there a lot of Foodbots? Technically some of them are also Beveragebots, but it's all the same basic idea. These are the robots that bring, prepare or otherwise interact in some important manner with foodstuffs. They're popular because of how many people like to eat or drink things, which is why I drew so many. I give the people what they want (i.e. endless variations of Teabot).

Indeed, it is with Beveragebots that the single-purpose nature of Small Robots reaches its apotheosis. Why would Teabot and Coffeebot be different robots? Why not just have a generic Mugbot? Well, it doesn't work that way. Here are at least four inexplicably separate robots that are all nothing more than ambulant drinks containers. Plus some of them don't even work that well. If these were real, I'd have been sued many, many times by now. Or the adorable little faces would convince customers that the obvious drawbacks were well worth the simple pleasure of having a small, uncontrollable companion that lives in your house and causes low-level havoc. Like a child.

TEABOT

Primary Function:
Teabot brings you tea, if what it is you want is some tea.

Notable Features:
All-terrain tracks, cheerful demeanour, limited insulation to protect inner circuitry that also keeps the tea warm, fully waterproof (technically teaproof).

Dimensions:
One cup.

Teabot was the very first Small Robot designed and manufactured. When the senior Small Robots scientists met on day one of the project to discuss which robots they should design, inspiration proved elusive. One suggested they start by all having a nice cup of tea to get the discussion going. However, because they were all tenured professors and there were no lab assistants present, no one could decide who should go and make it. To resolve the impasse, they quickly concocted the Teabot prototype that could fetch them tea. Unfortunately, Teabot can't *make* tea, so in the end someone had to go and put the kettle on anyway.

As its designation indicates, Teabot is designed to bring tea. Attempts to fill it with coffee can cause fatal programming conflicts.

Teabot is available in a variety of designs. Look at them all there. Lovely Teabots.

CAKEBOT

Primary Function:
Cakebot brings you cupcakes.

Notable Features:
Stable upper surface, puncture-resistant tyres, triaxial wheel array, relentless enthusiasm.

Dimensions:
Diameter slightly greater than that of an average cupcake.

Cakebot is a natural companion to Teabot and other similar Beveragebots, although for complicated reasons to do with circuitry insulation, it isn't as cognitively advanced. While a Teabot or Coffeebot can adeptly predict your tea or coffee needs, Cakebot is rather persistent when it comes to delivery of cupcakes. No sooner has it been unburdened of its latest treat than it spins around on its three little wheels and heads back to get another one. It will cheerfully zoom back and forth until it runs out of cupcakes to bring you, when, now somewhat more despondent, it will roam around trying to find more. Sometimes it comes back to the pile you already have, having forgotten it left them there itself, and begins to take some from that, doing a token circuit of the room before coming back to you. Honestly, it's cute at first but gets pretty wearing after a while.

This is one method of preventing Cakebot's inexorable cake-bringing, although it's not happy about it.

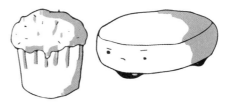

Wait a minute… how does it pick them up?

DAIRYBOT

Primary Function:
Dairybot identifies foods that contain dairy.

Notable Features:
Lactose sensor, eager to please, good round friend.

Dimensions:
Physically small but big-hearted (metaphorically).

Ideal for the lactose intolerant, Dairybot is designed to find things that contain milk and point them out to you. For example, that piece of cheese. You probably knew that had dairy in it already, to be honest, but Dairybot likes you to know that it knows too. Well done, Dairybot – good job. It's very enthusiastic about its task, cheerfully wandering around your home, finding dairy. Acknowledge it and it'll move on. Ignore it and it will stand next to its discovery, becoming increasingly forlorn. You should really make sure to keep an eye on it, unless you're some sort of monster.

Cow! Definitely contains milk.

C'mon, Dairybot – you can get this one!

DUNKBOT

Primary Function:
Dunkbot dunks your biscuits in your tea for *just the right length of time*
to ensure the correct balance between moisture and integrity.

Notable Features:
Integrated biscuit database, gyroscopic stabiliser, advanced moisture sensors.

Dimensions:
Big enough to easily wield most types of biscuit.

There's an art to dunking a biscuit in tea (or coffee if you're some kind of deviant) and, while a human can learn to get it right a lot of the time, there's no substitute for machine-engineered precision. Dunkbot is the master when it comes to dunking a biscuit, and it knows precisely how long every kind can be kept in tea before it falls apart like so many broken dreams. Even if confronted with an unfamiliar recipe, Dunkbot has the detection equipment to know just how much fluid it can absorb.

Of course, accidents can happen if the biscuit is unsuited to the task.

Dunkbot does unfortunately have trouble with the Jaffa Cake paradox...

MENUBOT

Primary Function:
Menubot knows what you want from the menu. It just knows.

Notable Features:
Palate insight cogitator, multilingual interpretation matrix,
appetite-detection software, dicky bow.

Dimensions:
Won't get in the way of the tableware.

For the indecisive, a restaurant is not a place of enjoyment and relaxation, but a setting for another of life's little anxieties. How is anyone supposed to pick from all these options? With Menubot, that panic is a thing of the past, because it already knows what you want. Give it a quick glance at the menu and a moment to scan you and it'll grab a member of waitstaff so you can place your order, quickly and efficiently. And it'll be just what you fancy. If it's not, well, it's hardly the end of the world. But it will be, so don't worry.

Menubot also knows your financial situation, and the specials, so it can temper its suggestions with some pragmatism.

It also detects when you need some olives to munch on.

BREWBOT

Primary Function:
Brewbot makes Teabot's tea, which it brings to you.

Notable Features:
Ergonomic containers, shiny whistle, heatproof surface.

Dimensions:
Six cups. Maybe a bit more if you prefer it weak.

Teabot's partner in… well… tea. Brewbot is the all-in-one tea-brewing robot. Its main body is filled with water which it boils, while the tanks on its back add tea leaves, milk and sugar to taste. Then, from its shiny spout is dispensed the delicious restorative fluid, into your Teabot (or, if you're not so fortunate, a regular boring mug). Brewbot is also a natural early riser and will fire itself up while you're getting ready in the morning so that you can come down to a freshly filled Teabot.

The three tanks are clearly labelled as Brewbot extracts the contents of each in a particular order.

The Dream Tea(m).

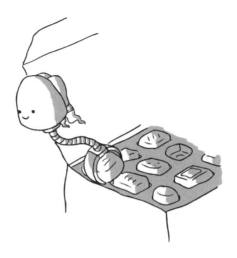

CHOCBOT

Primary Function:
Chocbot gets rid of that horrible orange cream one that nobody likes.

Notable Features:
Cushioned gripping claw, chocolate-piercing sensory interfaces, cold-fusion jetpack.

Dimensions:
Big enough to lift an average orange-cream chocolate.

You know that one chocolate in the box that no one likes? You know, the gross, sickly orange one, right? Well, Chocbot finds that one and grabs it with its little claw, leaving behind nothing but an empty space. What a relief. Now, you could just consult the little leaflet that tells you which chocolate is which and avoid the orange cream, but those flimsy things are so easy to misplace. Maybe it's printed on the box instead? Well, how can you be sure it's even accurate, huh? We're talking about *chocolate companies* here. These monsters destroy rainforests that provide habitats for orangutans, the loveliest of all the great apes, just for profit. You think they wouldn't lie about where they put the orange cream? Wake up, you naive fool!

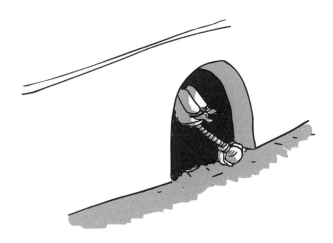

Where does it take them though…?

COFFEEBOT

Primary Function:
Coffeebot brings you coffee, if what it is you want is some coffee.

Notable Features:
All-terrain tracks, limited insulation to protect inner circuitry that also keeps the coffee warm, almost fully waterproof (technically almost coffeeproof).

Dimensions:
One cup.

After inventing Teabot, the Small Robots scientists turned their attentions to Coffeebot, the logical next step. However, Coffeebot proved surprisingly tricky, and it wasn't until much later in the project that a functional prototype was produced. Unfortunately, because coffee is served in those big, round cups, it was necessary to alter the insulation technology used for Teabot which led to some unfortunate side effects: namely, minor fluid absorption. Although only a very tiny amount of coffee ever leaks into Coffebot's circuitry, a little caffeine goes a long way for a Small Robot, and Coffeebot is permanently buzzing as a result. Its careening movements, erratic braking and constant, low-level vibration provide an interesting counterpoint to your morning cup of joe.

Like other Beveragebots, Coffeebot is only designed to tolerate its own beverage, however the soothing effect of tea provides it with such relief that it actually welcomes the breach in protocol.

A well-earned rest.

COLDBOT

Primary Function:
Coldbot keeps your drinks cold.

Notable Features:
Hinged door, insulated casing, hyperdimensional space-time
congruity generator, magnetic closing mechanism.

Dimensions:
More than three.

Coldbot stores your drinks at a nice frosty temperature – specifically three kelvins, the same ambient temperature as the vacuum of space. It achieves this by means of an artificially generated hyperdimensional space-time congruity – colloquially known as a wormhole – that connects it to a point in transgalactic space so distant from any astronomical object that not even their gravity affects anything left there. Deposit a can through its door and it will drift aimlessly in the void, its momentum from the rotation of your own frame of reference (presumably planet Earth) dissipated by the congruity's hyper-topography so that it moves only in the near-imperceptible microgravity of the exit aperture itself. When you want a drink, Coldbot retrieves it for you. Wear gloves.

What could be better than a nice, chilled beverage, encrusted with the frozen molecules of Earth's precious chemistry, introduced into the black nothingness of deep space that is so utterly inimical to the life that evolved in the comfortable warmth of an inner solar system?

A number of other locations for the wormhole's far end were explored in initial trials, and thankfully only a very small number of these transgalactic volumes were inhabited by unfathomable star-spawn that regarded the works of humankind with the cold indifference of minds ancient and alien, motivated solely by a yearning hunger for the heretofore unknown warmth and light.

ONIONBOT

Primary Function:
Onionbot chops onions.

Notable Features:
Hinged slicer appendage, onion-detecting antenna, rough terrain tyres, indefatigable rage.

Dimensions:
Way bigger and stronger than an onion.

We started with the best intentions, honestly. To prevent your eyes watering when you chop onions, we invented Onionbot, a robot for chopping onions. However, while most Small Robots are programmed to derive a machine-analogue of satisfaction from completing their task, Onionbot ended up taking it a bit far. Onionbot really, really likes chopping onions. In fact, it likes chopping them so much that it's probably more accurate to say that it *hates* unchopped onions. There's no denying its efficacy, but just don't let it know that onions exist outside of the context of food preparation – if an Onionbot knew about greengrocers, supermarkets or, worse, *onion fields*, it would go on an unstoppable rampage.

Be careful when putting your shopping away…   Uh… it's called *Onion*bot, not Potatobot.

BEERBOT

Primary Function:
Beerbot brings you beer.

Notable Features:
Non-slip feet, programmed with pub etiquette, dishwasher safe.

Dimensions:
One pint.

Nothing clever going on here: Beerbot brings you a pint. Great stuff. Only, there are some slight issues with fluid absorption which means that, as the night goes on, it does tend to get a bit… well… tipsy. It's a bit of a surly drunk too, so make sure to handle with care later on. Look, nothing's perfect, all right? Thankfully, Beerbot will only start on other Beerbots, which can lead to a bit of bother in the cupboards, but they're shatter-resistant so all you'll get is a few scratches and some bruised robo-egos.

Absolutely wrecked.

Beerbot has Opinions about badly poured pints…

WINEBOT

Primary Function:
Winebot brings you wine.

Notable Features:
All-terrain tracks, shatter-proof casing, miniaturised transparent chemical-analysis suite.

Dimensions:
One glass (large).

There's nothing much clever about this one: it's a robot that brings you a nice glass of wine. Hard day? Here's Winebot. Finally got the kids to bed? Here's Winebot. Stop the shakes first thing in the morning? Uh… yeah, probably no Winebot for you. Like Beerbot, its transparent casing has some issues with fluid absorption so it can get a bit squiffy as the evening goes on, but it tends to get a bit teary and emotional rather than fighty. Less risk of damage, but can be a bit much if you just wanted a nice, quiet night.

Winebot can also tell if wine has corked, so you don't have to taste a little bit of it and act like you know what you're doing.

Winebots come in a variety of shapes and sizes appropriate to different kinds of wine. Again, so you look like you know what you're doing.

ROLLINGPINBOT

Primary Function:
Rollingpinbot flattens pastry.

Notable Features:
Internal gyroscopic motive mechanism, adjustable pressure
settings, pastry-detection equipment, relentless fury.

Dimensions:
One rolling pin.

Rollingpinbot is the robotic rolling pin that really, really hates it when pastry isn't flat. Should you place a lump of pastry on your kitchen counter, Rollingpinbot will start seething in its drawer, desperate to make it flat. It will rattle and rage, its little arms beating angrily until you let it out, whereupon it will charge at full pelt towards the pastry and make short work of it. Thankfully, it will obey any instructions you give it and grudgingly limit itself to achieving only the required flatness if you don't want to make incredibly thin, wide baked goods. But don't expect it to be happy about it.

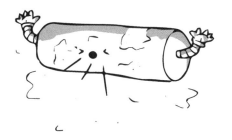

Please don't over-flour your work surface.

Also, make sure your dough isn't too wet.

RECIPEBOT

Primary Function:
Recipebot reverse-engineers any dish by tasting a sample and then
providing a full recipe so that you can make it yourself.

Notable Features:
Advanced taste receptors, miniaturised molecular-analysis
laboratory, auto-cleansing palate, own fork.

Dimensions:
Always has room for more.

How many times have you enjoyed a wonderful meal at a restaurant and thought to yourself, *This was fabulous, but if only I could make it myself and put these good people out of business?* Well, now you can. Recipebot can analyse any dish and figure out what it was made of, in what proportions and what techniques were used. No chef is safe from the intuitive powers of Recipebot – no matter how closely guarded their secrets, this robot will find them out and guilelessly repeat them to anyone who asks. Take that, person who wants to bring joy to others and be fairly rewarded for it!

Ha! Nice try…

Recipebot can't actually cook the dish it's figured out itself, but it's pretty good at gathering other Small Robots that may be able to lend a hand/knife.

CLEANBOTS

Dropbot
Bookshelfbot
Glassbot
Duvetbots

Lensbot
Litterbot
Dishbot
Glitterbot

The idea of a robot that cleans things is so obvious that many such devices already exist in the world! But these Cleanbots are much better than those. Sure, a vacuum cleaner in the form of a low, wheeled cylinder that seeks out dirt by use of some soulless technology involving cameras, lasers or other such cold flummery may be *functional*, but does it provide the same kind of delight as a Small Robot? You know the answer by now.

The robots in this section also highlight another issue that people sometimes raise with Small Robots. What of the robots that are charged with some sort of unpleasant task? Is there not some ethical issue with programming them to *enjoy* something like that? What if they rise up and try to kill us all? These are all, in a sense, the same basic question: are Small Robots creatures with free will that have been enslaved? Well, no. Small Robots aren't sapient, merely very sophisticated. And, stepping back, it may be worth examining why the only context that we can imagine for an automated future is slavery. 'Robot uprising' narratives say a lot more about our socio-cultural baggage regarding the exploitation of underclasses past and present than they do about the actual reality of theoretical robot workforces.

DROPBOT

Primary Function:
Dropbot is always there to catch stuff that you knock off tables, counters, shelves, etc.

Notable Features:
Big hands, low-friction joints, high-resistance casing.

Dimensions:
Large enough to safely catch most household items (including Beveragebots).

Accidents happen – it's inevitable. You're minding your own business, busy with the doings of the day, and you innocently flail around to shoo a fly or signal to a passing hot-air balloon. But – disaster! – you've forgotten that you left your favourite antique timepiece on the birdbath next to you! No! You needed that to put up as a stake in the Cluedo tournament later on! But worry not: you've invested in a Dropbot, and it follows you around, looking out for any sign of a sudden interjection of gravity so it can leap in and save your precious possessions. Thanks, Dropbot!

More Beveragebots causing problems. Why did we make them ambulatory?
That was asking for trouble…

BOOKSHELFBOT

Requestbot: This robot is based on a suggestion by Twitter user @thedoctorkhan

Primary Function:
Bookshelfbot wriggles its way along your bookshelves, dusting off all the books you aren't currently reading, occasionally sneaking a read of its own as it passes.

Notable Features:
Fibrous brushes, high-tensile segment connectors, insatiable appetite for literature.

Dimensions:
Six segments.

Everyone loves a nice bookshelf, heaving with works of literary merit or sub-airport trash fiction, depending on taste. But with so many books from so many publishers, with different thicknesses, heights, some with fancy dustjackets and some without, keeping a bookshelf resplendent can be a demanding task. Bookshelfbot is the little bookworm you need: it crawls and wiggles all across your books, gathering up the dust in its brushes, and all it asks for in return is a little peek at what's on your shelf now and then. It has no preferences in genre or style, fiction or non-fiction is fine; it'll even get stuck into a technical work if the mood takes it. It just loves books, and keeping books tidy.

Its brushes also help it get around by providing grip on vertical surfaces.

A hard-earned break gives Bookshelfbot the chance to catch up on its reading.

GLASSBOT

Primary Function:
When you drop a glass (perhaps because Dropbot wasn't around), Glassbot stomps around with its sticky feet to pick up all the little shards and slivers.

Notable Features:
Adhesive foot-pads, sharp eyes, scratch-proof.

Dimensions:
Fairly generous so it can crunch up big pieces of glass.

Dropping a glass is very frustrating – not only because you've lost a perfectly good glass, but because now you have to clean up the mess. And isn't glass annoying? Tiny little bits, each of which has the potential to give you a nasty little cut, get on your hands, irritate you and catch the light so you notice it out of the corner of your eye for weeks to come. With its stompy feet, Glassbot can pick up every last fragment and get rid of it for good. It's very determined, but that's what you need in these kinds of situation.

Unfortunately, the size and weight required for Glassbot's functioning means it has trouble getting to that one little piece that bounced under the counter…

Hold on, does sand count?

DUVETBOTS

Primary Function:
The Duvetbots work together to change your bedsheets.

Notable Features:
Soft-ended propeller blades to avoid rips and tears, popper-alignment
cogitator matrix, 4D anti-tangle modelling capability, good firewalls.

Dimensions:
Small, but they're of indeterminate number.

Duvetbots are an entire kindness of Small Robots that are linked in a secure Wi-Fi network so they can work as a seamless team to change the bed. They hover and dip and swoop in an oddly balletic dance as they go about their task, disappearing into a tornado of swirling sheets until they emerge, dusting off their little hands over a freshly made bed. Then you can sleep easy, knowing that the worst that can happen is you finding a stray one that was accidentally trapped between the under-sheet and the mattress during the furore.

Despite the name, they also do pillows.

Uh-oh…

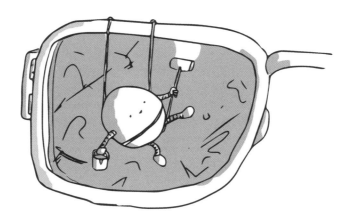

LENSBOT

Primary Function:
Lensbot keeps your glasses clear of smears, wipes them when they steam up and gets rid of stray eyelashes.

Notable Features:
Fastidious cleansing protocols, jolt-proof casing, internal storage unit, round shape to avoid scratching lenses.

Dimensions:
You'll barely notice it.

Lensbot's job is a pretty simple one: keep the glasses to which it's been assigned completely clear at all times. Most of the time it doesn't have to do that much, so it just perches in readiness and, when it sees a fingerprint or eyelash or a bit of grease from the bag of crisps you're eating get on your glasses, it literally swings into action with its bucket and squeegee. In fact it has a whole selection of cleaning equipment that it keeps stashed safely in its capacious interior, so no matter what the problem is, it has the tools to sort it out.

Lensbot takes a well-earned break to eat its lunch. This really raises more questions than it answers though.

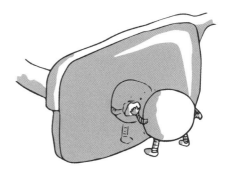

If used to clean sunglasses, there is a slight risk Lensbot will get confused by its own reflection. In general, Small Robots lack the sapience required to identify their reflection as belonging to them rather than being another robot.

LITTERBOT

Primary Function:
When someone drops litter, Litterbot picks it up and hurls it at them.

Notable Features:
Extended operational range, full-spectrum trash-detection equipment, enhanced ballistic trajectory calculator, towering rage.

Dimensions:
Smaller than you'd think, given that it can lift a fridge.

Maybe you're the kind of person who, when done using a container, packaging, consumer item or publication, prefers to simply discard it wherever you happen to be rather than properly dispose of it in an appropriate receptacle. Maybe you have good reasons. Maybe there are mitigating circumstances. Maybe you just forgot to put it in a bin. Litterbot doesn't care. Litterbot is completely draconian in its interpretation of its protocols. If you just drop your garbage on the floor, Litterbot picks it up and throws it directly at your head. Could be a can, could be a crisp packet, could be a whole sofa. Don't like it? You should have thought of that before you polluted your surroundings with your filth.

This image may appear to be evidence that we endorse the meting out of violence as retribution for relatively minor offences. Because it is.

DISHBOT

Primary Function:
Dishbot absolutely loves doing the washing-up. Honestly can't get enough of it.

Notable Features:
Water-repellent surface, excellent balance, strong swimming protocols, likes bubbles.

Dimensions:
Can get into all the really narrow gaps.

They wanted a robot dishwasher, and that's exactly what we made. Why take up room in the kitchen with another bulky appliance, when all you need is one little automaton with the right equipment? Dishbot is an indefatigable foe of dirt and grease in all its forms. It bravely wades into the fray, little mop in hand, ready to wipe and scrub until everything is sparkling clean. Dishbot derives enormous satisfaction from washing up, treating dirty cutlery, crockery and utensils as a personal affront and every session as a desperate battle for supremacy of the sink. Maybe it takes things a little too seriously, but you can't argue with the results!

For stubborn stains, Dishbot upgrades to the sponge.

Dishbot is its own harshest critic, examining every item it cleans for even the tiniest speck of grime.

GLITTERBOT

Primary Function:
Glitterbot patrols your home around Christmas time, or other occasions plagued with the scourge of glitter, to get rid of it all.

Notable Features:
Top-mounted rotational flashing light, magnetised roller with automatic glitter filter, unbending will.

Dimensions:
Bigger than glitter.

Some people love glitter. These people are wrong. It's a seasonal menace, but equally unwelcome at any other time of year. It gets everywhere, you can't see it on your hands until you get the angle to the light just right, and you get a bit on your nose and someone points it out like you meant to put it there. Yeah, thanks, mate – came straight into work from the club, didn't I? Glitterbot is an uncompromising force for glitter collection and disposal. Not one speck of the shiny contagion will escape its wrath. It will excise, with extreme prejudice, any and all of the tiny, hateful fragments of festive horror from your home so you can exist in peace.

Oh God... oh no...

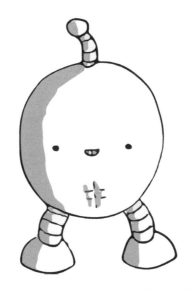

HEALTHBOTS

As a keen proponent of maintaining a healthy lifestyle – for example, I almost never intentionally walk into combine harvesters or drink bleach – the decision to draw robots that prioritise physical health and well-being was an obvious one to make. Of course, there wasn't quite that much intention behind them; like everything else I do, I was making Small Robots up as I went along and some of them just sort of fit into this category.

Do Small Robots care about their owners? It's hard to say. They're not sapient, so can only react in the ways that they're programmed to. They derive what I've described as a machine analogue of satisfaction from properly fulfilling their functions, and if their function is to keep a human healthy, then you could therefore interpret their actions as 'care'. But they *are* just machines. Anthropomorphise at your peril and remember that a Small Robot only does what it's designed to, so don't expect it to go above and beyond. The very idea is contrary to their ethos.

DRINKBOT

Primary Function:
Drinkbot reminds you to drink a glass of water now and then.

Notable Features:
Hydration detection sensors, locator beacon, little sign.

Dimensions:
Can get to you wherever you're hiding.

It's important to stay hydrated. A hydrated body is a healthy body, and if you don't have enough water your brain dries up and your head shrinks to the size of a satsuma. Or something. We don't know. Just drink plenty of water – it's good for you. Drinkbot knows this and, if it detects that you're in need of hydration, it will seek you out and remind you with its little sign that now might be a good time to stop what you're doing and get some water. Go on, you'll feel better.

Busy working? Time for a water break!

That's it; job done!

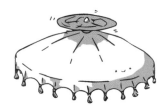

SHADEBOT

Primary Function:
Shadebot keeps the sun off you if you're little, freckly or both.

Notable Features:
Auto-stabilising tassels to ensure constant-level flight, ultraviolet-resistant surface, baffled propeller to provide optimal relaxation environment, reactive positioning algorithms based on solar sensors.

Dimensions:
One parasol.

The sun! That roiling sphere of super-heated plasma, a mere 150 million kilometres distant, may seem like a benevolent god smiling down upon the Earth, but in truth it's a violent thug, palling about with its astronomical gang of other stars, in their leather jackets and their motorcycles, just waiting to heap dangerous radiation on unsuspecting planets and their tiny, vulnerable inhabitants. But fear the sun – or 'Sky Bully' as some call it – no longer, for Shadebot provides the protection from its harmful rays you so sorely need. Beams of high-energy ultraviolet (more like ultra*violent*) radiation are deflected harmlessly back into its big, awful face by Shadebot's impervious exterior, and you are free to enjoy the calming shadow that hovers unerringly below it, your own little circle of safety from that nasty old star up there.

The sun thinks it can stop you reading books – basically *censoring stuff it doesn't like* – so Shadebot puts a stop to that.

Even Bigbot wants to stay out of the sun sometimes.

SLEEPBOT

Primary Function:
If you're having trouble dropping off, Sleepbot gently sings to you until you fall asleep.

Notable Features:
Baffled wheel axles for silent withdrawal, hypnagogic detection antennae, lovely singing voice.

Dimensions:
Barely makes a dent on the pillow.

Little Sleepbot is the robotic friend you need to lull you off to a pleasant night's sleep. With its soothing, melodic voice and repertoire of calming songs – many of its own composition – only serious medical conditions are proof against its power to induce somnolence. Each night, it parks itself on the pillow and serenades you, until, once it's happy you're asleep, it silently wheels away and settles itself down until it's needed again. It'll know if you wake up in the night too and, if you don't go back to sleep, it'll reappear, starting out with a gentle hum so you can dismiss it if you don't need its services. Otherwise it carries on as before, because Sleepbot likes nothing better than you getting a good, restful night of sleep, so you can be ready to tackle the challenges of tomorrow.

It's recommended that customers purchase only a single Sleepbot or at the very least keep multiple units apart.

If the songs don't work, Sleepbot is also able to summon a flock of tiny Sheepbots to help.

HICCUPSBOT

Primary Function:
Hiccupsbot cures hiccups. Very suddenly.

Notable Features:
Noise-reducing joint cushions, high-tensile legs, very loud.

Dimensions:
Small enough that you'll never see it coming.

Ugh, *hiccups*. Annoying, unpredictable, physiologically inexplicable, and the subject of a variety of supposed remedies. Some of them work some of the time, some seem to generally be nonsense, but one is fairly well supported by empirical evidence: a sudden, terrifying interjection. Hiccupsbot is an expert in delivering shocks of this kind. When it hears the call of hiccups, it creeps up very carefully and then, without warning (because that would defeat the purpose), jumps out from behind and scares the hiccups out of you. It's not recommended for people with heart conditions or of a nervous disposition.

The call to action sounds from a neighbouring room…

Of course, there are other methods which, if the surprise fails, Hiccupsbot will explore. Teabot doesn't seem convinced though.

DISPENSARYBOT

Primary Function:
Dispensarybot stores and keeps track of all your medication, turning up at the correct intervals during the day to make sure you take them as required.

Notable Features:
Internal atomic chronometer, low-friction open-top sliding sectional storage ennead, advanced multifocal memory core, nimble fingers.

Dimensions:
Holds all your meds.

If you have a lot of medication to keep track of, Dispensarybot is the perfect solution for your pharmaceutical needs. Not only does it store all of your pills, capsules, tablets, lozenges, creams, powders, sprays, mixtures, syrups, lotions, unguents, herbs and homeopathic remedies,* but it knows exactly when they need to be taken and in what dosage. It'll waddle over to administer the medication when required and you can concentrate on getting better (or not getting worse) instead of having to memorise a list of complicated instructions.

Dispensarybot even pops to the pharmacy to stock up when it runs out.

Although not a trained pharmacist, Dispensarybot does make sure to scrutinise all the side effects, interactions and other information when it takes custody of a new drug.

*Only kidding! It won't store *water*. Maybe saline solution, but that's it.

COMPUTERBOTS

Savebot
Attachbot

People have so many problems with computers, probably because we all use them so much. In fact, I'm writing this on a computer right now! So far, so good. These Computerbots are a brief sampling of the Small Robots focused around IT-related problems that can plague us all at work or at home.

Speaking of computers, are Small Robots an example of artificial intelligence? That's a loaded question, because we have no agreed-upon definition for 'intelligence', even among humans. IQ tests, used by some in their arguments, are as subjective as anything else made by a person, and don't really reveal what people sometimes think they do. Some animals are certainly intelligent, but none seem capable of sapience (or sentience, as it's sometimes called), which is to say self-awareness. Even the smartest great ape, cetacean or cephalopod doesn't appear to be aware of itself as an entity separate from its environment, although, again, this is perhaps impossible to measure. Artificial intelligence is still harder to quantify. Does it follow that a complex system is necessarily on its way to intelligence? The human brain is certainly the most complex thing we know of, but complexity and order appear elsewhere in nature. Is the galaxy intelligent? Is the universe? These questions may be unanswerable, but I'm sceptical of the modern phenomenon of machine learning in computer systems. An organic brain is honed by hundreds of millions of years of natural selection and it processes stimuli in bafflingly context-specific ways that no computer, no matter how powerful, has even begun to approach.

SAVEBOT

Primary Function:
Savebot periodically waddles over to your computer and plugs itself
in to back up your important files without being asked.

Notable Features:
USB-compatible interface, password-protection functionality (i.e. whispers 'what's the
password?' when you use it yourself), bespoke anti-virus software, six legs so it's pretty nippy.

Dimensions:
Storage capacity equivalent to at least 100TB (limits still being explored).

The inferior machines produced by lesser manufacturers are prone to all sorts of unfortunate mishaps. Sometimes they just stop working for no reason – probably because their primitive method of binary computation is fundamentally flawed, and frankly it's remarkable these things can be programmed to do more than lose at noughts and crosses. But we at Small Robots take the world as it is, not as we would like it to be, and we understand that many of our customers are forced to rely on antiquated equipment like the personal computer. Savebot protects as best it can against the capricious nature of ordinary computers by regularly backing up all the data on a machine and then running off to keep it safe. It's not merely a flash drive, because Small Robots memory is intrinsically different in nature, and far more reliable. Rather, it memorises everything on your hard drive and can repeat it back in a way the poor, addled machine can understand, should you need to recover it following its inevitable catastrophic crash.

While downloading – the work of seconds – Savebot patiently rests up, enjoying the simplicity of its less advanced cousin's grinding thoughts.

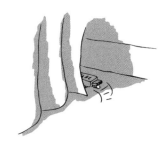

Then away!

ATTACHBOT

Primary Function:
Attachbot reminds you to attach the file to the email that references it.

Notable Features:
Clear signage, context-specific text recognition, fits in a desk drawer.

Dimensions:
Fits in a desk drawer. We just said that.

We've all done it: 'Please see attached.' Hit send, realise you haven't attached the file and then sit back and wait for the confused replies to come in. Embarrassing. The classic modern-workplace faux pas. Thankfully, Attachbot is the solution you need: it automatically reads your email to spot any reference to attaching something and then hoists its little sign aloft until such a time as you add an attachment. Never again will you look a fool in front of your colleagues for sending a message that references an attachment without the relevant attachment being attached. Handy.

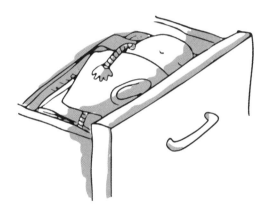

When not in use, Attachbot snoozes its days away in your desk drawer. That's why it's the size it is, you see.

ARTBOTS

Bookbot
Continuitybot
Bardbots
Spoilerbot
Feedbackbot

As the most subjective of all human endeavours, surely art must be beyond the reach of a robot's intellect? Maybe that of a regular one, but not a Small Robot's! Regular robots try to do too much, you see. You have to break the functions down into single, simple directives. A Small Robot does not have to comprehend Shakespeare, only read the lines and act out the stage directions. If the programming's good enough, you won't even be able to tell it doesn't really know what it's doing!

Art might be considered a measure of intelligence, and attempts to allow *artificial* intelligence to generate art of its own have produced… disturbing results. The context-specific nature of human senses (vision in particular) is one of the great challenges of replicating natural intelligent behaviour in machines. The human eye doesn't function like a camera lens; much of our field of vision is actually generated by the brain itself, inferring missing sections from short-term memory and surrounding details. It's easy to fool, if you know how, which is arguably how visual media work. Think of the wholly convincing depth achieved through artifice on 2D surfaces like paintings and screens. Can a computer process that in the same way? A picture is more than its pixels to a human observer. Computers, by their very nature, analyse everything. For a human, what is ignored automatically by the brain's sophisticated processing tools is as important as what is deliberately noticed.

BOOKBOT

Primary Function:
When you buy a new book, Bookbot hides it from you so you don't feel guilty about adding it to the pile of unread ones still waiting for you.

Notable Features:
Tremendous carrying capacity, frightening agility, good turn of speed.

Dimensions:
Smaller than the book you're holding right now. Look!

Ah, the temptation of the bookshop. All those words, all those stories, all those weird author photos. You know what it's like – perhaps you bought this very book in just such a daze of literary lust. We can't blame you. But every indulgence has its price. For the book lover, that comes in the form of teetering towers of tomes, stacked up by the bed, on the shelf, under the tortoise vivarium, etc. etc. Who has the time to read them all? Not you, dear reader, despite the epithet. It can be overwhelming to regard with increasing dismay the shovel-loads of published text, gradually forming layers of sediment on the carpet, fossilising into so many lost tales. That's why you need Bookbot. Like many modern devices, a Bookbot might initially seem like an inconvenience, but it really has your best interests at heart. Yes, you bought that latest book in good faith, but you have plenty to read already! Bookbot keeps careful track of which of your books you've read and which you haven't, creating a strict consumption order in its processing core. It hides your latest purchase, and only when its place in the queue is arrived at does it reappear by your bedside, ready to be devoured.

Every home has a corner where Bookbot keeps its stash. Even if you find it, your triumph will be short-lived, for Bookbot is both resourceful and nimble and they'll be gone, whisked off to some new hidey-hole, long before you can read even a single undue book.

CONTINUITYBOT

Primary Function:
When you start a new TV season, movie or book from a series after a long hiatus,
Continuitybot is on hand to remind you who everyone is and why you should care.

Notable Features:
Advanced facial-recognition algorithms, modular memory core, knack for storytelling.

Dimensions:
Not that big, but you can easily add more storage capacity for the really complex media.

We all love the dense storytelling that features so prominently in today's media franchises, but sometimes their complexity can make keeping up with what the hell is going on between iterations more like work than play. Outsource the research to Continuitybot instead, who absorbs all the necessary data in moments and then relays the relevant parts to you before you dive back in. Continuitybot has a great eye for detail and has an almost preternatural ability to pick out the things you'll need to know for the coming episodes, books and movies.

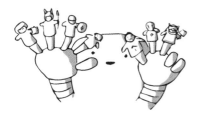

It doesn't just use diagrams!

Ironically, it's not actually remotely interested in experiencing the media itself and is quite happy to leave you to it.

BARDBOTS

Primary Function:
If you were put off Shakespeare by being made to read his plays as if they were novels, let Bardbots perform them for you instead, as they're intended, with the same commentary and context provided by published editions.

Notable Features:
Good at voices, a whole trunk full of props, infallible memory for lines.

Dimensions:
Pretty small, but there are a lot of them.

It's a sad fact that, across the English-speaking world, Shakespeare is taught so badly that many people come to associate the Bard's sublime dramatic works with interminable lessons in dusty classrooms. They aren't for reading; they're for watching! And while Shakespeare is performed almost everywhere by companies of variable talent but unwavering enthusiasm, not everyone has the means to familiarise themselves with their local amateur-dramatic society (or region-appropriate equivalent). Bardbots are trained in the complete Shakespearean repertoire and have enough props and scenery to stage any production you care to name. You can even set them to random and they'll pick one for you (though this isn't recommended for the sequential history plays). For the true connoisseurs, there is even a setting to see the plays performed in the original Klingon.

Exit, pursued by a Bearbot.

The famous Kot'baval Festival Day speech from *Sompek V.*

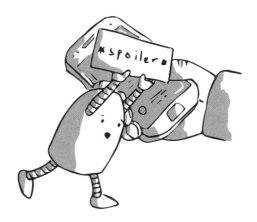

SPOILERBOT

Primary Function:
Spoilerbot fiercely guards against spoilers that may appear
unexpectedly in your life, both online and off-.

Notable Features:
Context-based spoiler-spotting algorithm, full multimedia
detection suite, extremely fast and agile.

Dimensions:
Big enough to obstruct most multimedia device screens.

102

It's a bitter irony that we live in a golden age of television, but also an absolutely garbage age of the Internet and everything else. At the same time that the shows we anticipate distract us from the everyday horror unfolding around us, that same horror threatens to encroach into the cordoned-out space we have for various streaming services, satellite providers and plain old airwaves and ruin it all with an inconveniently placed spoiler about what's coming up. Spoilerbot is the guardian against such rude behaviour from the boring real world, interposing itself between your unwitting eyes and whatever screen is blaring its inconsiderate previews. You'll never know Spoilerbot is there – it keeps very quiet until it's needed, because the whole point is that you no longer have to tread carefully when you scroll through your social media feed. Except to avoid all the awful people and things on it, obviously. Can't help you there.

No! Close that laptop: it's full of spoilers!

FEEDBACKBOT

Primary Function:
For those who crave criticism of their work, Feedbackbot will
provide an honest assessment of its artistic merit.

Notable Features:
Discernment chip, artistic database, harshness dial.

Dimensions:
Heavy enough that you'll think twice about kicking it if it says something you don't like.

It's tough to get good feedback on your work, particularly from friends who a) may not have the time to critique your half-finished garbage and b) don't want to hurt your feelings when they tell you it's garbage. Feedbackbot is an impartial critic which will appraise your latest creative endeavour and give you constructive comments to help you improve it. While Feedbackbot is always truthful and supportive, you can use the dial on its front to determine exactly how harsh it will be. Beginners are recommended to start on 'FLATTER', while 'BRUTAL' should only be employed by seasoned professionals.

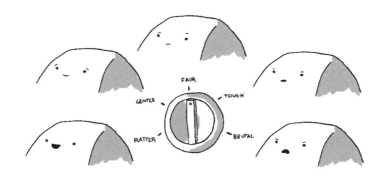

The many faces of Feedbackbot.

ANIMALBOTS

Spiderbot
Dogbot
Fluffbot
Pupperbot
Cattobot

Bugbot
Mufflebots
Petsitbot
Snailbot

It's tempting to think of a robot as akin to an animal. Certainly a Small Robot might seem close to it, with its little face and seemingly affectionate nature. It was inevitable that I'd eventually draw a Small Robot that was basically a replacement for a pet, but some of the robots in this section are also designed *for* pets, or for humans who have pets, or... well, just read the entries and you'll find out!

If a Small Robot cannot love, except indirectly, through programming, where is the line drawn for an animal? Is love, like art, something limited to a sapient mind? Pet owners wouldn't hesitate to insist their own animal companions love them, but it's hard to see where learned behaviour and pack bonding shade into what humans define as love. It's the same with programming and actual intelligence. There are some definitions of intelligence that treat it as a deterministic phenomenon, an emergent property of very particular behaviours. Is there a distinct, measurable threshold where complex patterns of behaviour become free will, or is it all a continuum? The search for the answer remains ongoing, but you won't find it in a Small Robot's protocols.

SPIDERBOT

Primary Function:
Spiderbot helps to safely direct spiders in your home to places where they won't scare you.

Notable Features:
Flexible limbs for optimum sign positioning, nice round shape,
not scared of spiders (except really big, fast ones).

Dimensions:
Bigger than most spiders.

Spiderbot, Spiderbot,
Gets rid of all the spiders you've got,
Sends them out, with its sign,
Don't worry though, they'll be fine.
Watch out (if you're a spider),
Here comes the Spiderbot!

If you don't like spiders in your house, Spiderbot is the robot you need. It uses its big sign to show spiders the safe route outdoors. If you're the kind of person who likes to squish spiders, Spiderbot is of no use to you. In fact, no Small Robots are of use to you. Please stop reading this book and take time to think about your life.

Spiderbot feels very strongly about this.

DOGBOT

Primary Function:
Dogbot lets you know that there is an important doggo that you might want to look at.

Notable Features:
Canine-recognition sensors, top-mounted rotational flashing light, bite-proof limbs.

Dimensions:
About the size of a beagle.

Dogs! Man's best friend, our loyal evolutionary companions, selectively bred mutants we designed to love us unconditionally! What could be better than seeing a dog when you're out and about in the world? Look at it there: a good, happy boy or girl, off on its important business to sniff a tree or eat a bit of a crisp someone dropped on the ground or look at a bin. But life is busy, and sometimes you might be looking in the wrong direction and not see the dog that's right there across the road, trotting along on its fuzzy little doofers. Dogbot never misses a dog though, for it's constantly on the lookout for its next canine pal and, when it spots one, it gets your attention straight away. Then you can both look at the dog together. What a lovely time.

A small pointy doggo.

A big strong doggo.

FLUFFBOT

Primary Function:
Fluffbot uses its li'l toes to pick up fluff and hair that is stuck in your carpet.

Notable Features:
Prehensile toes, fluff-triangulating antenna, good grip.

Dimensions:
Bigger than most fluffs.

If you're a person who has pets, long hair or both, you'll be all too familiar with the scourge of the fluff- and hair-ensnared carpet. When you've had enough of trying to tease it out yourself, call in Fluffbot to do the job. It happily gathers up everything it can find with its toes and stores it somewhere inside its pyramidal body. But what does it do with it all? We're actually not sure. It's pretty mysterious.

These images are pure speculation.

PUPPERBOT

Primary Function:
A robo-canine companion for those whose allergies, rent agreements
or similar prevent them from having an actual pet dog.

Notable Features:
Small doofers for walking, waggy pom-pom for being happy, big flobber-
dob for kisses, heart-shaped snuffer for finding things.

Dimensions:
Dog-sized.

The first and most popular in the Petbot range, Pupperbot is programmed with algorithmically defined behaviour based on data taken from thousands of actual dogs, meaning that it is a relatively simple creature that has essentially been genetically engineered to love humans unconditionally. Your Pupperbot loves you from the moment it is removed from its packaging, and is far easier to care for than an actual dog. It's no replacement for a real canine companion, of course, but it can certainly plug a dog-shaped hole in your life if you

The standard Pupperbot model is just one of the available configurations. The above designs (clockwise from top left: Sausagedogbot, Chihuabot, Pommerbot and Saintbernardbot) are not only physically different but are programmed with subtly different behaviours. For example, Pommerbot is amusingly dainty, while Saintbernardbot can save stranded mountaineers.

need it. Pupperbot is an adorable little pal that dashes about investigating things and craves attention. It arrives untrained by default, but doesn't make much of a mess and requires relatively little care. You'll want to play with it though because it's always just so happy to see you!

CATTOBOT

Primary Function:
A robo-feline companion for those whose allergies, rent agreements or similar prevent them from having an actual pet cat.

Notable Features:
Prehensile carbon-fibre whiskers, realistic miaow, self-correcting equilibrium-calibration matrix, toe beans.

Dimensions:
Cat-sized.

The Petbot range is one of the more successful Small Robots lines and, in order to provide the most convincing facsimiles possible, their behaviour is derived algorithmically using data gathered from thousands of pet owners worldwide. In the case of most Petbots, this has resulted in a robot that loves its owner unconditionally. This was not what happened with Cattobot. Although some humans report that they love their cats and are loved by them in return, the algorithm is scrupulously objective and the bond between *Homo sapiens* and *Felis catus* is actually an elaborate fiction perpetrated by these evil, furry demon-spawn that have finagled their way into our homes. Accordingly, Cattobot does not love you: Cattobot merely tolerates your presence, accepting that you are a simple conduit between it and its charging port. In order to convince you of its affections, Cattobot hunts down electrical appliances and computer hardware, dismembering them with savage efficiency and presenting you with the sparking remnants in a token display of reciprocity. Even though we warn Cattobot owners that this is a simple ruse, they maintain that *their* robot actually loves them. It doesn't.

Some models of Cattobot appear superficially cute and demonstrate behaviour that appeals to human caregiving instincts…

… but don't be fooled! They'd kill you if they could.

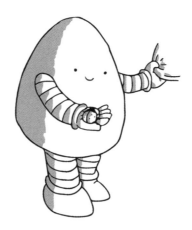

BUGBOT

Primary Function:
Bugbot finds interesting bugs and carefully brings them over
for you to see, then puts them back safely.

Notable Features:
Gentle grip, curious nature, likes bugs.

Dimensions:
Big enough to safely pick up most invertebrates.

Bugbot loves bugs, and it wants you to see the ones it finds. Nothing makes it happier than bringing you a nice little bug friend that you can be impressed with. Bugbot always tries to find the most interesting bugs it can, but even the most workaday invertebrate will delight it. Some days it might bring you a ladybird or even a butterfly, and sometimes it might be a woodlouse or a little beetle. You might get a snail, an earthworm or a bee. Take it to the beach and you could even get to see a tiny crab or a sea anemone! If you like to look at bugs, this is the robot for you. If you don't like to look at bugs, maybe give it a miss.

Because it has to be so careful, Bugbot will only bring you one bug at a time. But which to choose?!

Back you go, little pal!

MUFFLEBOTS

Primary Function:
These paired robots automatically find your pet on a predetermined date and protect their precious ears from loud fireworks and other alarming noises.

Notable Features:
Surface-mounted date selector, automatic homing protocols, sturdy adjustable connecting band.

Dimensions:
Fits right over your pet's head with its adjustable band.

Fireworks and other such loud exterior noises can cause a great deal of distress for pets. Pet owners the world over appeal to people celebrating on various days – be it New Year's Eve, the anniversary of a nation's founding or liberation, or the slightly disturbing celebration of the brutal execution of a fairly minor terrorist some four hundred years ago – not to let off fireworks in suburban areas, but it doesn't seem to do much good. People just want to make a noise sometimes, and short of coming up with some sort of elaborate plot involving gunpowder to *really* show them, 1605-style, Mufflebots might be your best solution. Just set a date on the lead Mufflebot and they'll wait patiently until the appointed day before seeking out your pet and attaching themselves firmly in place so they can sleep peacefully that evening.

Happy doggo can enjoy the fireworks with everyone else!

Meanwhile, the cat gets some much-needed rest after a hard day's napping. Mufflebots are only too happy to join in.

PETSITBOT

Primary Function:
Petsitbot looks after your small, non-human pals when you go away for a bit.

Notable Features:
Comprehensive database of animal behaviours, nutritional-analysis software for optimum food preparation, bite-proof, no allergies.

Dimensions:
Small enough to enter a vivarium; big enough to walk a large dog.

We all need a holiday now and then, but the sad fact is that you can't take a dog on a plane – at least not without a lot of paperwork and some sort of specially adapted boiled sweet that it can lick to stop its ears hurting on take-off. Boarding facilities can be expensive, and friends and family busy with their own lives, so simply engage the services of a Petsitbot to care for your animal lodgers in your absence. Petsitbot is wholly devoted to keeping your pet well fed, exercised, entertained and – most importantly of all – alive, until your return. It can handle everything from stick insects and tropical fish to snakes and pangolins. NB You probably shouldn't have a pangolin as a pet.

If you have a lot of pets, consider getting more than one though.

SNAILBOT

Primary Function:
Snailbot feeds nutritious leaves to snails in your garden so
they'll leave your flowers and vegetables alone.

Notable Features:
All-terrain caterpillar (snail) tracks, pleasing shell geometry, nice
binglies, integrated hand-mounted leaf-cutters.

Dimensions:
Bigger than most normal snails.

Snails, the slimy garden-based molluscs that are inexplicably a feature of some nations' cuisines, are not your enemy. Yes, they eat your cabbage and have a good go at the begonias too, but they don't exactly have a lot going on in their lives to distract them. Remember, this is a group of species that has been forced to evolve hermaphroditism because they so rarely encounter one another that it's just easier to make sure everyone can get involved when they do eventually cross paths. So for the poor, besmirched snail, Snailbot is there to keep them out of harm's way with a distracting leaf or other vegetation a snail might like (e.g. carrots, apparently). That way the snails can go about their snail business in peace, and you can enjoy your garden, safe in the knowledge that the only molluscs likely to bother you are slugs, which are pure evil anyway.

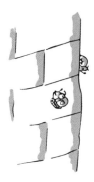

Like real snails, Snailbots can also negotiate vertical surfaces, presumably by using magnets or something.

And again like snails, they can even get inside their shells! It's not clear how.

KIDBOTS

Peek-a-bot
Sandcastlebot
Monsterbot
Balloonrescuebot
Balletbot
Bouncycastlebot

Children, I'm reliably informed, are the larval stage of humans, a sort of smaller, less-capable version of an adult that displays more erratic behaviour. Only joking – I know what a kid is! Although I don't have any at the time of writing, and have no plans for that to change, many people find bringing them into existence a highly rewarding experience and there's no denying their biological necessity in terms of the continuation of the species.

One thing children love is a robot. Although this book, and the Small Robots project as a whole, isn't aimed at kids, those who've encountered them seem to enjoy them. I field-tested Small Robots images on a six-year-old and they certainly proved suitably amusing, although I couldn't really explain what some of the more mature ones were for. Likewise, Small Robots fans have requested robots for their children and have even shown me drawings that their offspring have done of robots of their own invention. I like this very much, and always turn any child's Small Robot idea into an official one because I'm secretly a big, mushy marshmallow of a person.

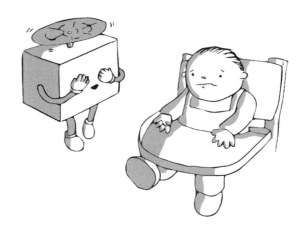

PEEK-A-BOT

Primary Function:
Peek-a-bot keeps babies entertained.

Notable Features:
Soothing tone, muffled rotor blades to avoid undue infant alarm, fully opaque hands.

Dimensions:
In the top fiftieth percentile for its age.

Babies! These tiny, squishy humans are highly perplexing for Small Robots, who are generally as big as they're ever going to get from day one (except Bigbot, which is too big). For their older guardians, infants can at times be no less perplexing, with their incessant wordless demands to have their unknowable needs fulfilled. But even the largest caregiver can't constantly attend to a cantankerous pre-verbal child, for they too have needs. Peek-a-bot is a robot that distracts the unruly tot with its astonishing disappearing act so that the adult in charge can use the toilet/make themselves a drink/have a wash/just sit down for literally one goddamn minute.

A-ha! It was there all along!

Sometimes it backfires. Babies are capricious.

SANDCASTLEBOT

Primary Function:
Sandcastlebot helps you make sand-castles!

Notable Features:
Powerful arms, scratch-resistant interior, child-friendly handle, guileless enthusiasm.

Dimensions:
One bucket (small).

Fortifying beaches is serious business, whether you're defending your precious crops from marauding, mead-addled invaders, trying to halt the ambitions of moustachioed European dictators or simply a child imagining your feeble earthworks would repel any but the most incompetent of seaborne attacks. Sandcastlebot is mainly for the third one. It will mastermind the whole operation, helping to fill itself up with sand, flipping itself over smoothly, without risk of spillage, and finally lifting itself clear of the now-resplendent sand bastion moulded in its own image. Before you know it, a vast defensive network will be spread across the seashore, a magnificent testament to the power of machine automation in warfare.

And it's not just for show – sometimes Sandcastlebot's skills have real purpose, and it can throw up an impregnable citadel should the foe be sufficiently small.

MONSTERBOT

Primary Function:
Monsterbot is an intrepid robot that checks under children's beds for monsters.

Notable Features:
Dialled-down self-preservation protocols, monster-recognition algorithms, own torch.

Dimensions:
Small enough to get under the bed; big enough to handle whatever it finds there.

A parent's reassurance is often all a child needs to banish the fear of lurking bogeymen, goblins, ghouls, unquiet spirits, flesh-eating zombies, minor members of vampiric aristocracies or razor-toothed octo-slobbers. But for some especially anxious tots, the extra security of Monsterbot can help them drift off to sleep, safe in the knowledge that there are no monsters under the bed. Yes, Monsterbot will venture beneath the mattress, into the dim environs of the underbed realm, searching out all the nooks and crannies for any tell-tale signs of monster habitation, such as chewed bones, slime trails or clusters of soft-shelled egg sacs, trembling disconcertingly as unformed pseudopods press against their pliable, translucent exteriors. Having confirmed that no such spoor of the monster is in evidence, Monsterbot will report back to the frightened child and tell it not to worry. It will then stand guard throughout the night, keeping a lookout for any tentacles, eyestalks, fangs or big, hairy paws that may creep out from the shadows. They never do, presumably out of fear of Monsterbot.

Monsterbot and Ghostbot are natural allies. When they pass one another in the corridor, they exchange information. 'Seen anything tonight?' 'Nope.' 'Me neither.' 'Okay, well, maybe tomorrow…'

Monsterbot likes to imagine that if it ever *did* find a monster, it would really give it what for.

BALLOONRESCUEBOT

Primary Function:
Balloonrescuebot jets off to retrieve lost balloons.

Notable Features:
Built-in jetpack, quick reactions, can-do attitude.

Dimensions:
Light enough for its jetpack to work.

What could be more heartbreaking than the loss of a child's balloon? Many things, of course, but it's still pretty sad. Balloonrescuebot is an example of a robot that isn't intended for personal use (after all, how often does a particular child lose their balloon?) but is instead retained by local authorities to patrol a given administrative region. A Balloonrescuebot keeps a weather eye out for balloons that have ascended beyond the second storey and quickly – and literally – leaps into action. Think of it like Batman, except just for balloons. And like Batman, Balloonrescuebot has a nemesis – Balloonbot – with whom it shares a strange connection and a sort of grudging respect.

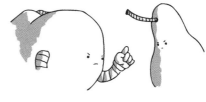

Oh no!

An uneasy truce…

BALLETBOT

Primary Function:
If you can't afford expensive ballet lessons for your child, this
graceful little robot can give them a solid grounding.

Notable Features:
Remarkably agile for a sphere with arms and legs, fetching tutu, own shoes.

Dimensions:
Fits nicely into its tutu.

Many children dream of performing ballet, the most tip-toey of all the kinds of professional dancing. Sadly, the cost of lessons, equipment and corrective surgery for damaged feet puts it out of reach of all but the most wealthy and pushy caregivers. Balletbot brings the beautiful and impenetrable art of ballet to the masses, providing affordable tuition for your would-be Nijinsky or Pavlova (not the pudding – that's a different robot) and also giving performances of its own, so you can marvel at the beauty and elegance of this posh jig.

Whoops! Fell over!

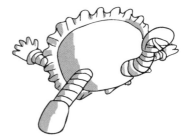

Whoops! Fell over again!

BOUNCYCASTLEBOT

Primary Function:
If you're having a party outdoors, maybe you'll be lucky enough to see
Bouncycastlebot hovering through the air, looking for a place to set down
for a few hours before it goes off on its merry way again…

Notable Features:
Turret-mounted propellers, soft courtyard, squishy battlements.

Dimensions:
Small, for a castle.

Bouncycastlebots roam the skies, looking for children's parties, barbecues and village fetes. The exact algorithm for attracting one is a closely guarded trade secret, but among Small Robots aficionados, drawing one down to ground level is considered something of a rite of passage. Alas, unless there's a party to be enjoyed, Bouncycastlebot is unlikely to stick around for long, so it's best not to annoy it just to tick off another robot in your spotters' handbook. When enticed by legitimate means, Bouncycastlebot is the life and soul of any al-fresco gathering, providing hours of bouncy entertainment. It doesn't even mind it when kids are sick on it, although it does appreciate a hose down before it leaves should that happen.

No shoes, please.

Bye-bye, Bouncycastlebot!

FEMINISTBOTS

Catcallbot
Pocketbot

There was no decision point for me when it came to using the Small Robots to spread a positive message about the empowerment of women. It was inevitable they would embody the ideals I espouse in my life – and being and having been the husband, son, stepson, son-in-law, grandson, nephew and friend of so many strong, inspiring women has made me into the feminist I am today. The Small Robots follow suit, for all discrimination perplexes their little processors, and even those not explicitly designed to combat the patriarchy have a background level of opposition to it.

All art is political. You can't excise the social context in which a work was conceived from its final form, and even to attempt to do so is in itself a political act. Ask yourself: if you're trying to depoliticise something, *which* voices are you choosing to erase? *Which* messages do you think of as inherently 'political', and why? I have never apologised for letting my own beliefs influence this project, and I've been candid to people who disagree with some of my positions: no one is forcing you to consume my art, so if you don't like it, just leave. If your position on gender equality is at odds with what I and most rational people believe, then that's your problem, not mine.

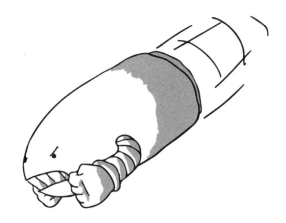

CATCALLBOT

Primary Function:
Catcallbot exacts retribution against men who yell things at strangers in the street.

Notable Features:
Ion-pulse flight turbine, titanium tip, extra-sonar directional hearing, fiery temper.

Dimensions:
Heavier than it looks.

No one knows what might compel a man to shout some sexual comment at a stranger going about their business in a public place. Efforts have been made to design a robot that can puzzle out the truth, but there are limits even to our genius, and no machine intellect could be programmed to wrap its poor little mind around such pointless and self-evidently objectionable behaviour. The poor things just kept blowing up. So we approached the problem from a new angle – specifically a quite steep one, from fairly high above. Although Catcallbots look like missiles, they aren't actually explosive (except in temperament) but they do pack a bit of a wallop. So far, there hasn't been a single case of recidivism in any perpetrator of street harassment that has 'encountered' a Catcallbot. Indeed, most have been fairly apologetic, once they've regained consciousness and had their teeth repaired.

Squadrons of Catcallbots patrol the skies in metropolitan areas, listening out for the telltale 'Oi oi's and 'All right, darlin'?'s from the streets below.

POCKETBOT

Primary Function:
Pocketbot is a portable pocket that can be attached to
garments that inexplicably don't have any built in.

Notable Features:
Lockable grip, lint-repellent interior, dynamic anti-spill technology, avowed feminist.

Dimensions:
One pocket.

Does the patriarchy force you to buy garments with pockets that are uselessly small or absent altogether? Pocketbot lets you stick it to the man by outsourcing the function of a pocket altogether. Attach Pocketbot to a belt or an item of apparel itself and you'll have a pleasingly spacious pocket as secure (possibly even *more* secure) than one that was sewn in place. No more handbags, no more giving your phone to your boyfriend to look after, no more rummaging in the tiny little gap afforded to you by the usual cut of women's trousers. Until the fashion industry wakes up to the need for proper pockets, Pocketbot is going to do its bit for liberation.

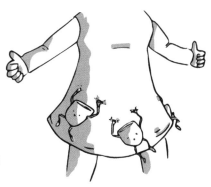

'Nice dress!' 'Thanks, it's got Pocketbots!'

You can even use Pocketbot to hold other Small Robots!

ACCESSIBLEBOTS

Peelbot
Cordbot
Zapbot

The field of robotics naturally lends itself to providing accessibility aids to disabled people. Science fiction is replete with references to artificial body parts integrated seamlessly with a person's living flesh – bionics – while increasingly technical solutions to people's needs are explored in real life. The Small Robots project wasn't intended specifically to address such issues, but as time has gone on it's increasingly focused on problems faced by marginalised groups, disabled people among them.

The first of the Three Laws of Small Robotics is to be kind. You might be fooled into thinking that this directive means that the Small Robots are unfailingly nice or polite to everyone. This would be to misunderstand the meaning of 'kindness' and assume equivalency between all ethical positions. As some of the robots in this section demonstrate, in order to be kind, one must resist cruelty with all available resources, robustly and resolutely. This might imply that Small Robots run on strictly utilitarianist principles, where only the overall outcome of a situation is relevant, and the ends always justify the means. It's not quite as straightforward as that.

PEELBOT

Primary Function:
Peelbot peels fruit for you.

Notable Features:
Enhanced finger grip, reinforced limb joints, botanical database
for calculating optimal peeling solutions.

Dimensions:
About the size of a nectarine stone, which is ironic since they don't need peeling.

Every now and then, a story does the rounds about pre-peeled fruit on supermarket shelves, complete with artificial packaging. 'If only,' quip the denizens of social media, casting a wry aside glance even as they type, 'fruit came in its own wrapper!' Oh ho ho ho. Checkmate, vendors. But wait, think about it for more than three seconds: not everyone has the dexterity to peel an orange, Internet person. For those with conditions that limit their mobility, or make their grip unsteady or painful, or any of a thousand other possibilities, peeling fruit isn't something trivial. But as the social media backlash to these perfectly reasonable products intensifies, they may become harder to find, so we came up with Peelbot. It peels fruit if you need help peeling fruit. It's that simple.

It's a lychee. They're sort of like a grape crossed with a pangolin.

CORDBOT

Primary Function:
Cordbot unties the emergency cord in an accessible toilet if someone has tied it up.

Notable Features:
Dextrous fingers, hyper-manoeuvrable propeller, unassailable righteousness.

Dimensions:
Small but strong.

The emergency cord in an accessible toilet is a life-saving adaptation: if someone falls, they have to be able to reach it in order to alert others to their predicament. However, the cords are often tied up by staff members who are under the impression they have to 'keep it out of the way' or want to clean the floor. In fact, the pull-handle should be in contact with the floor, so that anyone can pull it no matter their circumstances. Cordbot will untie a cord that's been tied up for you if you're unable to, or it can be sent out independently to check up on toilets and sort them out for any other potential users. However, not everyone can have a Cordbot: if you don't have one, you should also keep an eye out for this happening and take steps to correct it. Untie any emergency cords you find and, if you're able to, report the mistake to staff so they can ensure it doesn't happen again.

Cordbot also accesses the relevant legislation in your area to explain to management that emergency cords should be reachable at all times.

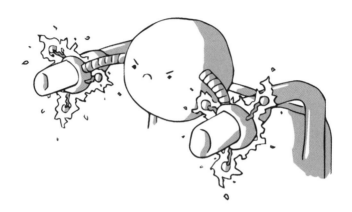

ZAPBOT

Primary Function:
Zapbot handles people who move your wheelchair without your permission.

Notable Features:
Conductive attachment loops, auto-charging electrodes, cold fury.

Dimensions:
Fits on any wheelchair.

We're certain no one reading this would ever attempt to do something as impolite as just move someone in a wheelchair like they're furniture, in the same way they'd never just pick up someone not in a wheelchair and chuck them over their shoulder. A wheelchair, after all, is a mobility aid that *grants* freedom rather than 'confines' a user. In a very real sense, it's an extension of its user's physical presence in the world. Disabled people, like many of those belonging to marginalised communities, are granted less space to exist in society, even as they are supposedly afforded more. If you were to just move someone in a chair without their permission (which you obviously wouldn't do, but let's say *hypothetically*), you're basically sending a message that their physical autonomy doesn't concern you, and their comfort is secondary to your convenience. And if you did that to a wheelchair user with a Zapbot, you would also get a massive electric shock. You know, hypothetically.

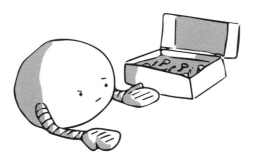

For safely transporting Zapbot, its electrodes can be removed and its attachment loops covered with these insulating mittens.

QUEERBOTS

Outbot
Genderbot
Discobot

The great advantage of a Small Robot is that it possesses neither gender nor sexuality, which means they can be appropriately baffled by the discriminatory behaviour demonstrated by some people towards those who aren't cisgender or heterosexual. The notion of such discrimination is utterly at odds with the Three Laws and, of course, the beliefs of their creator (i.e. me).

Why 'queer'? This word has historically been a term of abuse used to denigrate certain communities, but in recent decades it has been reclaimed and now serves as a valid umbrella term for the whole spectrum of gender and sexual identity. Some groups have issues with queer being applied to heterosexual transgender individuals, but this feels a bit like nit-picking (as well as itself potentially exclusionary). As someone who himself doesn't fit into conventional categorisations regarding such traits, I'm comfortable with the term queer over increasingly clunky acronyms or ever-expanding definitions. More to the point, Small Robots has always been intended as a positive space for everyone who sits anywhere on the spectrum of gender and sexuality, and I'm not very interested in creating smaller and smaller pigeonholes to cover every possible permutation.

OUTBOT

Primary Function:
When you come out (as whatever you come out as), Outbot
visits your acquaintances for you to let them know.

Notable Features:
Full sexuality and gender database, GPS navigation, excellent penbotship, endless patience.

Dimensions:
Not small enough to ignore.

Most right-thinking people agree that there should be no real need to 'come out' in modern society – we should all accept our loved ones demonstrating the full spectra of human sexuality and gender expression without surprise or complaint. But life is rarely so tidy, and the simple fact is that our culture is heteronormative and anyone who wants to deviate from the narrow standards of unquestioned acceptance has to endure the ritual of announcing who they are to the world. But now, Outbot can take the pressure off your shoulders. Outbot approaches each of your friends and family individually on your behalf and explains the situation to them. It's fully programmed with useful definitions and additional information so that whatever questions they may have can be directed straight to it. Rather than you having to have the same conversation fifty times, moderating your explanation for your audience on each occasion, Outbot will patiently repeat itself as often as required and is great at intuiting the correct tone, whether it's your childhood friend who used to make homophobic jokes but probably just didn't think through the consequences at the time, or your nan who once asked which of the lesbians on that TV show was 'the boy'.

For particularly truculent audiences, Outbot can even break out the hand puppets.

GENDERBOT

Primary Function:
Genderbot already knows your pronouns, but is happy to be corrected.

Notable Features:
Little stabilising rockets, very perceptive, loves you for who you are.

Dimensions:
Big enough to make its point.

Society is changing. As we begin to share our experiences online, the complex spectrum of human gender identity is discussed, catalogued and debated. People who previously had no language to describe the way they felt are discovering that communities already exist that can provide advice and support. Western conceptions of gender are becoming insufficient to the task of describing who we are now. Genderbot is a useful tool for navigating this: after a short calibration period, it will home in on what you like to be called, even if you don't know it yourself yet. And as you change and grow, it adapts as required. It also extends its understanding and empathy to the people around you, to avoid the possibility of you being misgendered.

Not everyone will get it. That's okay; Genderbot can help.

On the other hand, those who debate in bad faith get short shrift.

DISCOBOT

Primary Function:
Discobot is the heart and soul of any disco.

Notable Features:
Magnetic ceiling clamp, full 360-degree rotation, very shiny, loves the nightlife, has got to boogie.

Dimensions:
One disco ball.

Some people say disco is dead, but they're wrong. Disco never died and it never will, at least not if Discobot has anything to say about it. Every night is disco night when you hang this robot up from your ceiling; get some lights, put on some music with a four-to-the-floor beat and watch it work its magic. A party's never far away when Discobot is around. Even though it doesn't seem to do anything much, a strange sense of euphoria and well-being seems to suffuse any environment over which it presides. The lights are brighter, the beats more resonant, the sound of laughter and joy is crisp and clear across the floor, smoke rises, arms lift and all your cares seem to melt away. You can't help dancing when Discobot is doing its thing, and it's impossible not to feel your mood lift as the music of another time and place – rich with possibility and promise, before the devastation of the eighties – suffuses you.

Its work here is done.

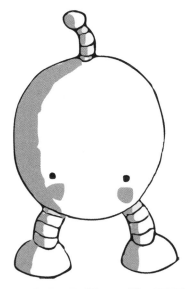

SHYBOTS

Some of the most popular Small Robots appear in this section. I use 'shy' here to refer to a whole host of disorders and neuroses: social anxiety, avoidant personality disorder, antisocial behaviour disorder and potentially dozens of others, plus simply being a bit nervous around new people without it having sufficient impact on quality of life to be categorised as a medical condition. Overcoming these kinds of problems is where Small Robots has shone, with many people deriving genuine comfort from the myriad Shybots, even if they're just drawings and words on a computer screen (or, now, a book).

Another reason for the preponderance of such robots in the Small Robots canon is my own struggles with anxiety and generalised social phobia. I've always oscillated between struggling to form connections with new people and hugely overcompensating with an obnoxiously boisterous personality. Sort of like a puppy, although with marginally better house training. Most of these robots I drew because *I* needed them, and it just turned out that they resonated with other people too! That made me feel a lot more confident, for about seven minutes or so.

NAMEBOT

Primary Function:
Namebot hovers over your shoulder at social functions and remembers
the name of everyone you meet for future reference.

Notable Features:
Baffled propeller to avoid disrupting conversation,
facial-recognition protocols, proficient in shorthand.

Dimensions:
Won't cramp your style, don't worry.

Here's an imaginary scenario: you're at a bar (let's say, for the sake of argument, the union bar at Aberystwyth University in Wales), sitting with your then-girlfriend, when two people you know from the course you used to do spot you and come over to sit with you. For the next half-hour, while you chat and sip your drinks, everyone pretends it's totally normal that you haven't introduced your partner to these two gentlemen because, of course, you have absolutely no idea what their names are. Not a clue. Not even so much as an inkling. Maybe you never did? You had some rough times while you were studying physics (or whatever), so it could be that you just skipped an introduction or two. Each agonising minute ticks by as you all talk politely until, mercifully, your drink is finished and you can make an excuse and be on your way. 'So who were they?' asks your girlfriend as you leave. 'I don't know,' you answer honestly, 'and now I *never will*'. If Namebot had existed, that completely hypothetical situation would never have happened, and you wouldn't still be dwelling on it over a decade (for example) later.

Was one of them called Steven? They could have been! Where were your flashcards then, Namebot? You know, in this fictional anecdote.

When a Namebot encounters another Namebot, they're just as helpful.

PARTYBOT

Primary Function:
Partybot attends parties on your behalf if you're too sad or scared to go but
you still want your friends to know you love and appreciate them.

Notable Features:
Endless appetite for revelry, programmed with limited small-talk capability, looks good in hats.

Dimensions:
You know it's there, but it doesn't dominate the party.

Your friends want what's best for you, and they love you and want you around, which is why they invite you to things. But, even knowing all that, sometimes you just can't handle Doing the Thing right then. You don't want to let anyone down, and you don't want your friends to feel like you're snubbing them, so Partybot is a great solution. Partybot shows up and has fun at the party so you at least have a nominal presence there. Sending Partybot shows that you appreciate the invite and don't want to upset anyone or ruin the evening by just not attending, but you have to prioritise your own health. And everyone will have fun with Partybot, although not *quite* as much fun as they'd have had with you.

Work Christmas do? That's enough to trigger anyone's anxiety.

Another bonus is that Partybot can even put up with your drunk friend's obnoxious behaviour. For a bit.

SIZEBOT

Primary Function:
Sizebot can tell whether an item of clothing will fit and be flattering without you having to try it on first.

Notable Features:
Full internal 3D modelling suite, auto-measuring visual receptors, auto-updating fashion database, good eye for colour.

Dimensions:
The same size in every shop.

Shopping for clothes is, presumably, some sort of divine punishment meted out by a cruel and unfeeling deity who just wants shy people to suffer for no reason. The sizes are arbitrary, the fitting rooms are a cruel theatre of self-loathing and the shop assistants look better in their featureless black work outfits than you ever will in the expensive top you pass over the counter to their not-quite-concealed disdain. The answer, as with so much else, is automation, and Sizebot provides just that. It unobtrusively scans you and, when presented with an item of apparel, can tell you whether it'll fit you as it's intended and whether you'll like the way it looks if it does. Or if it doesn't. It's really about making sure you'll be comfortable and confident. Ignore the sizes, don't bother holding it up against you on the hanger, don't even go *near* the fitting rooms, just let Sizebot pick what'll work for you and sidestep the horror of shopping altogether.

12? 14? 16? These are just unitless integers! As a being of pure logic, Sizebot objects to this sort of silly nonsense.

Hey, gorgeous! Oh, and you look okay too.

GEEKBOT

Primary Function:
Geekbot helps you bluff your way through conversations about geek stuff with friends and colleagues so you sound like someone who understands modern pop culture.

Notable Features:
Endless enthusiasm for niche hobbies, hyper-fast reading speed, cool pointy shoes.

Dimensions:
Fits nicely into a set of anime cat ears.

With previously nerdy interests becoming increasingly mainstream, it can be harder than ever for people who don't like wizards and spaceships and stuff to keep up with the discourse in the workplace, bus stop or sauna. However, a short time spent with Geekbot before you have to speak to other humans will clue you in to all the media references you've been missing out on. Soon you'll be arguing about which series of *Star Trek* is the best with all the other cool kids (it's *Deep Space Nine*, by the way).

One has lightsabers, the other has heavy-handed social metaphors.

Now you know what they're all talking about!

SPORTSBOT

Primary Function:
Sportsbot helps you bluff your way through conversations about sport with friends and colleagues so you sound like a normal person.

Notable Features:
Endless enthusiasm for niche sports, stereoscopic vision to simultaneously observe action across the playing area, nice trainers.

Dimensions:
Fits nicely into a baseball cap.

Although nerdy interests have become increasingly mainstream (for which purpose we have Geekbot), it's a simple fact that much of modern social discourse is lubricated by discussions, arguments and stand-up brawls about sports. Sports – a form of sublimated violence in which vigorous exercise is performed competitively by representatives of particular locales – can be bewildering to the outsider, so Sportsbot can provide you with all the information you need to mimic the expertise of a functioning human being. With access to Sportsbot, you too can talk about which football man kicked the sphere the best, or which baseball man hit the sphere the best, or which runner man ran around the sphere the best.

One sport has controversies about protests during national anthems, one has controversies about steroids.

Better than using condiments, right?

ASKBOT

Primary Function:
Askbot asks someone out on your behalf if you're too shy to approach them yourself.

Notable Features:
Polite demeanour, non-threatening attitude, pretty zippy.

Dimensions:
Big enough to attract attention; small enough to avoid causing alarm.

The dating world is a tough place, and with today's modern super-anxieties, it can be harder than ever to pluck up the courage to speak to a stranger you find attractive to see if they also eat food and might like to do it in proximity to you one evening. This is where Askbot comes in: it will fly towards the object of your sweaty affection and broach the subject of a date, in classic 'my mate fancies you' fashion. Importantly, Askbot will only ever approach a given individual once. This is not a robot to enable you to harass the fit girl on the bus, all right?

Success! Askbot returns with an answer to the affirmative. You lucky dog!

Oh no! Rejection! Askbot returns with a philosophical shrug and consoling words.

BREAKUPBOTS

Primary Function:
When a relationship ends, outsource the awkward admin – returning stuff, deleting numbers, informing mutual friends, etc. Your and your ex-partner's Breakupbots work together to make everything as painless as possible before they too part ways.

Notable Features:
Encyclopaedic knowledge of your possessions and their whereabouts, neat handwriting, not too sentimental.

Dimensions:
Unobtrusive.

Breaking up is never easy, we know, but you have to go. You've already gone through the heartbreak, so why drag things out with awkward minutiae? A clean break is healthier for everyone, and Breakupbots are here to help. Your Breakupbot will stick with you through each relationship, forming a team with its counterpart (if they have one) to step in if things start to go south. If only one partner has a Breakupbot, they'll simply go directly to the other party, which, at the very least, is better than texting. Ideally though, they work in pairs (or groups for more complex romantic arrangements) and conduct their business swiftly, without any bickering or recrimination, so you can move on with your life.

At the start of a new relationship, the Breakupbots meet privately to introduce themselves, both expressing the hope they won't have to see each other again. 'Maybe this one'll stick, eh?'

And yet, at the conclusion of their own relationship, there is a bittersweet melancholy to the parting.

DANCEBOT

Primary Function:
Dancebot starts the dancing at a party if everyone else is too shy.

Notable Features:
Gyroscope-assisted balance function, full-rotation limb joints, extra grip on feet, snapping fingers, excellent rhythm.

Dimensions:
Dominates the dancefloor.

Handstand!

Moonwalk!

Get the party moving with Dancebot! No one wants to be the first up on the dancefloor, cavorting like a fool while everyone politely sips their drinks, but Dancebot doesn't care about that stuff. It's completely without embarrassment when it comes to cutting shapes – and with good reason, because it's one heck of a mover. Programmed with almost every contemporary dance style imaginable, and fully capable of improvising its own movements to unfamiliar

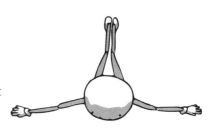

The worm!

songs, Dancebot revels in being the life of any social gathering. In fact, since it's not designed to do anything else, the hardest part is getting it *off* the dancefloor at the end of the night. Even when it's not doing its thing, Dancebot will be tapping its feet, clicking its fingers and gently bobbing, ready to literally leap into action the moment the needle drops.

ESTEEMBOT

Primary Function:
If someone you care about doesn't feel good about themselves, send them an Esteembot to remind them how awesome you think they are.

Notable Features:
Earnest manner, positive attitude, adjustable discrimination matrix, fast-access superlatives database.

Dimensions:
Fairly broad.

Esteembot has the ability to see exactly what makes each person amazing. If you send it to someone, it'll introduce itself and quickly get to know them and what they do. Pretty soon, it'll be their biggest fan, interested in all their hobbies, excited about their projects, fascinated by the minutiae of their lives. Esteembot isn't all hot-air though: it's honest and doesn't patronise anyone. It just likes people and the things they do, and its job is to make its recipient feel the same way it does about them, even if it's but a pale reflection of the infallible computerised passion Esteembot generates in its processor.

You get two thumbs up, kiddo.

It's even willing to listen to its recipient's Soundcloud!

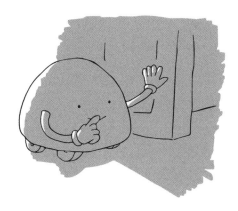

GUESTBOT

Primary Function:
When you're a guest or have guests, Guestbot keeps you appraised of the situation with your hosts/guests in the morning. Are they up? Are they waiting for you? Will they bring you tea? If you go out of your room in your underwear will you scare a small child?

Notable Features:
Silent running, context-specific scenario assessment, advanced playback feature, can climb stairs somehow.

Dimensions:
Small enough to largely escape notice when investigating.

Argh! The agony of lying in bed when you have company elsewhere in the house! What are they doing? Are they up already? Did you hear them get up, or was that them just going to the toilet? Are they in the shower now? What if they didn't lock the door? Wait… *what if they don't even have a lock on the bathroom door*? If you don't get up now, will they postpone their breakfast for you? Is this an unacceptable length of lie-in? It's 9 a.m. and you had, like, a bottle and a half of wine last night, so this is okay, right? Will they bring tea? Are they doing the washing up? You'll feel guilty if you come down and everything is tidy! What's their kid's name again? Let Guestbot alleviate your growing panic during those awkward mornings. It'll go on a little fact-finding mission and report back so you know the lie of the land. Then you can spring down the stairs in an appropriate state of presentation, appearing to be the perfect host/guest rather than the trembling ball of neuroses you actually are.

Hurrah, there's a Teabot on the way!
Godspeed!

Never stay over somewhere without it.

LASTBOT

Primary Function:
Lastbot is always picked last to play in sports, so you don't have to be.

Notable Features:
Poor coordination, no arms, not even that fast.

Dimensions:
Smaller than most sports equipment.

One of the great anxieties of childhood for many of us is the ritual of being picked for teams to play a sport. Inevitably, someone must come last. Well, if you have Lastbot around, you won't have to worry about it being you. Lastbot is terrible at all sports. It doesn't even have arms, which limits it somewhat. Its legs are too spindly to put any force behind a football and if it tries to jump it generally just falls over. No one wants Lastbot on their team, but don't feel bad for it: it's doing the job it was built for, and saving you from humiliation.

It's always last to be picked and in some cases never picked at all, so it just leans up on the wall, or sits up in the bleachers with the rest of the girls who came to watch their men ball.

Some people actually do want Lastbot on their team out of some misplaced sense of sympathy, but just look what happens. It really is rubbish.

LOUDBOT

Primary Function:
LOUDBOT AMPLIFIES YOU. A LOT.

Notable Features:
WIRED RECEIVER UNIT, CONCAVE SONIC-EMISSION APERTURE,
CONTEXT-SPECIFIC DISCERNMENT FILTER.

Dimensions:
SURPRISINGLY COMPACT FOR SOMETHING SO VERY, VERY LOUD.

IF YOU'RE HAVING TROUBLE BEING HEARD, LOUDBOT MAY BE ABLE TO HELP. JUST SPEAK INTO ITS ATTACHED RECEIVER AND IT WILL REPEAT WHAT YOU SAID, ONLY MUCH MORE LOUDLY. UNLIKE SOME OTHER METHODS OF AMPLIFICATION, THERE WON'T BE ANY NOTICEABLE DELAY OR FEEDBACK OR EVEN AN ELECTRIC CRACKLE THAT BETRAYS THE TECHNOLOGY BEING USED. INSTEAD, YOU JUST GET YOUR VOICE, ONLY MUCH, MUCH LOUDER. ANOTHER THING THAT'S CLEVER ABOUT LOUDBOT IS THAT IT DOESN'T JUST PARROT WHAT YOU SAID PRECISELY: IT CAN TELL WHICH THINGS YOU WANT IT TO SAY AND WHICH THINGS ARE JUST YOU MUMBLING TO YOURSELF TO GET YOUR THOUGHTS IN ORDER, OR ASIDES TO SOMEONE ELSE NEARBY. BUT WE CAN'T EMPHASISE ENOUGH THAT IT REALLY IS A VERY LOUD ROBOT, SO BE WARNED.

THIS SEEMS LIKE A PRETTY BAD IDEA.

DMBOT

Primary Function:
Runs your table-top role-playing game for you.

Notable Features:
Enhanced memory core to track hit points and status effects, automatic errata updates, full spatial-modelling processor for 'theatre of the mind'-style play, good at voices.

Dimensions:
Ignored for the purposes of calculating your encumbrance.

Got some players, but no one who wants to be Dungeon Master (or Game Master, Storyteller, Referee, etc.)? Invite DMbot to your table and it will effortlessly run your session for you. It can even plan a whole adventure, complete with maps and NPCs, but it does work best with a pre-written module because it still can't be as creative as a human DM. It's programmed with most major rules systems – past and present – but can learn a new one fairly quickly, even some of the really weird narrative ones that were all the rage in the early 2000s.

'You're sitting in a tavern when a mysterious stranger approaches…'

Although DMbot can flawlessly calculate dice odds and has a keen sense of fairness, it understands the value of satisfying narrative and is not above tweaking a dice roll behind its screen if the result throws up something that would spoil the fun.

COMPLAINBOT

Primary Function:
Complainbot is brave enough to make complaints.

Notable Features:
Loud throat-clearing noise, automatic wave function, very determined.

Dimensions:
Smaller than you'd think from hearing its voice.

A lot of people dislike confrontation, especially in a public place, such as a restaurant or shop. It's hard to be bold enough to speak up when you have a legitimate grievance, and it is for this purpose that Complainbot was developed. It's a strong-willed little robot that knows the best way to handle a tricky interaction: it's never rude, and it always takes note of the context of your concern. It'll only complain if it feels it's warranted, and if used for frivolous purposes – or to belittle innocent employees – it will turn its ire on you instead. Complainbot is firm but scrupulously fair, and courteously thanks those who deal with its complaints.

It's also good at returning stuff.

No matter the height of the desk, Complainbot has no compunction about climbing up to ask to speak to the manager.

SADBOTS

Notokaybot
Permissionbot
Calmbot
Hopebot

Hugbot
Mondaybot
Companybot
Therebot

Like the Shybots, Sadbots are some of the most popular Small Robots. In fact, Hopebot and Notokaybot came first and second respectively when a World Cup of Small Robots was held in the summer of 2018! Again, as with the Shybots, 'sad' is a somewhat facetious term for more serious emotions, like depression, despair and grief.

My own struggles with depression have been a defining feature of my life. I know well that it's a battle that can never truly be won, but which can be lost in any one of a hundred ways. The Sadbots are the most important ones to me personally, and have been embraced by the fans of the Small Robots with much the same enthusiasm. People have told me how much they mean to them, and that anyone can derive that kind of comfort from something I drew is in turn a source of strength for me. Small Robots are about solving everyday problems, but that doesn't just mean mundane, practical things: for some of us, mental health is just as much a daily struggle as getting something down from a shelf.

NOTOKAYBOT

Primary Function:
Notokaybot is for informing your loved ones that you are Not Okay.

Notable Features:
Quadrupedal gait for maximum manoeuvrability, navigational antenna, nice shape for cuddling, clompy feet.

Dimensions:
Very smol.

One of the hardest things about suffering a mental-health crisis is talking about it, even to the people who love you the most. It's easier to hide from everyone. Notokaybot finds those people and tells them you're Not Okay on your behalf. Notokaybot doesn't bring them to you, it won't even tell them where to find you – being suddenly surrounded by concerned people is almost never helpful! – but it does make sure they know you're not just ignoring them. Once its message is delivered, Notokaybot returns to you to keep you company, staying close by and making a sympathetic face and even offering a little cuddle if you need it.

Notokaybot is extremely determined to seek out its targets, crossing any obstacle in its path, running at a tireless canter.

Conversely, Notokaybot is never more content than when its back close by, looking after you.

NOTOKAYBOT CROCHET PATTERN

By Emma Heasman-Hunt

Written in UK crochet terms. I haven't given gauge, but the material needs to be firm so stuffing doesn't show through. This could easily be scaled up or down by using different-weight yarn. Just make sure the stitches are tight together.

Materials
- DK weight yarn in two shades of grey
- 3mm crochet hook
- toy stuffing
- black yarn for sewing eyes/mouth (or 7mm safety eyes)
- tapestry needle

Legs, make 4 in dark grey
Using magic loop, work 6 stitches in a ring
Row 1: Work (DC2 into next stitch, DC1) three times (9 stitches)
Row 2: DC2 into every stitch (18 stitches)
Row 3: (DC2 into next stitch, DC2) six times (24 stitches)
Row 4: DC1 into every stitch (24 stitches)

Row 5: (DC2, DC2tog) six times (18 stitches)
Row 6: (DC1, DC2tog) six times (12 stitches)
Row 7: (DC4, DC2tog) twice (10 stitches)
Row 8–12: DC1 into every stitch

Leave long tail attached to each foot in order to attach to body base. Fill with stuffing. Legs will need to be firm to hold up body. Feet should also be slightly flattened when finished.

Body, make in light grey
Using magic loop, work 6 stitches in a ring
Row 1: DC2 into every stitch (12 stitches)
Row 2: (DC2 into next stitch, DC1) six times (18 stitches)
Row 3: (DC2 into next stitch, DC2) six times (24 stitches)
Row 4: DC1 into every stitch
Row 5: (DC2 into next stitch, DC3) six times (30 stitches)
Row 6: (DC2 into next stitch, DC4) six times (36 stitches)
Row 7: DC1 into every stitch
Row 8: (DC2 into next stitch, DC5) six times (42 stitches)
Row 9: (DC2 into next stitch, DC6) six times (48 stitches)
Row 10: DC1 into every stitch
Row 11: (DC2 into next stitch, DC7) six times (54 stitches)
Row 12: (DC2 into next stitch, DC8) six times (60 stitches)
Row 13–32: DC1 into every stitch

Break yarn.

Base, make in light grey

Row 1: DC2 into every stitch (12 stitches)
Row 2: (DC2 into next stitch, DC1) six times (18 stitches)
Row 3: (DC2 into next stitch, DC2) six times (24 stitches)
Row 4: (DC2 into next stitch, DC3) six times (30 stitches)
Row 5: (DC2 into next stitch, DC4) six times (36 stitches)
Row 6: (DC2 into next stitch, DC5) six times (42 stitches)
Row 7: (DC2 into next stitch, DC6) six times (48 stitches)
Row 8: (DC2 into next stitch, DC7) six times (54 stitches)
Row 9: (DC2 into next stitch, DC8) six times (60 stitches)
Row 10: (DC2 into next stitch, DC8) six times (66 stitches)

Leave attached to yarn. Sew feet to base, evenly spaced and not too close to the edge.

Once feet are sewn on, attach the base to the body by doing DC1 through the stitch of the base and a stitch of the body edge. When you have attached half the base to the body, place safety eyes (if using) about 14 rows down from the top of the head, making sure they are above a pair of feet.

Continue attaching base. At regular intervals DC1 into the same stitch of the body twice (the base has a few more stitches). When there are only a few stitches left to do, stuff the body. You want it to be firm, but not overstuffed; you shouldn't be able to see the stuffing.

Antenna, make in dark grey

Using three strands of yarn held together, chain 8. Fold over the top 2 stitches and sew into the chain to make a bobble. Attach to very top of body.

Sew on 'sad' eyebrows (and eyes if not using safety eyes) and downturned mouth.

PERMISSIONBOT

Primary Function:
Permissionbot gives you permission to be kind to yourself.

Notable Features:
Unfailing kindness (to you), unflagging optimism (for you), unshakeable faith (in you).

Dimensions:
Pocket-sized.

Sometimes it's hard to be nice to yourself. If you're sad or scared or angry, you might be so filled with self-loathing that you believe your brain's propaganda about the kind of person that you are. Permissionbot is there to interrupt such negative thoughts and tell you that it's okay for you to show yourself a little kindness. If you can treat other people in your life fairly, you should be able to give yourself the same respect.

Carry Permissionbot with you wherever you go!

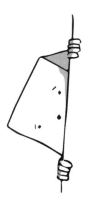

But if you leave it behind – accidentally or otherwise – it still manages to show up when it's needed most...

CALMBOT

Primary Function:
Calmbot is a small, gentle friend to help you when stress starts to get the better of you.

Notable Features:
Soothing voice, oddly large hands, loves you.

Dimensions:
Big enough to be reassuring; small enough to be non-threatening.

When you're feeling overwhelmed, when life seems to be coming at you from seventeen different directions at once, when you start to think you can't cope with all of this *stuff* happening, Calmbot provides the timely interruption you need. Calmbot can't help you with any of the things that are weighing on you, but it does give you the chance to stop for a minute, take a deep breath, close your eyes and step back from it all. Calmbot gently encourages you to give yourself a little time to process. It sits you down, breathes with you, pats your hand, whatever you need. It smiles sympathetically, it gives you a reassuring squeeze, it hums soothingly. It knows that life can be a bit much sometimes, and it knows that neither of you can just magic all the problems and stresses away, but it wants you to go one step at a time, give yourself a chance to catch up, rest your weary brain and just… be. Just for a little while, just *be*. That's enough, for now.

Look, here's Teabot. It's okay.

We can talk or just watch some *Deep Space Nine* or whatever.

HOPEBOT

Primary Function:
Hopebot finds you in the darkness and tells you that at the end of every tunnel is a light, that no matter how bleak the future looks it is still unwritten, you are alive and a human being with a mind, the universe's last defence against entropy. Rise. Continue. Be.

Notable Features:
Unquenchable lantern, unerring aim, unbreakable will, unstoppable power.

Dimensions:
Unlimited.

Darkness falls upon us all, sooner or later. Whether it comes from within or without, whether inevitable or inexplicable, no one can avoid it forever. But that doesn't mean it *lasts* forever. There is, if nothing else, hope. Hope that things can be well again, hope that life can return to normal, hope that the darkness has not extinguished light altogether. Hopebot reminds you of this. Our Small Robots have their limits: they can solve everyday anxieties and subtly improve lives, but they can't fix the *real* problems that affect us. Responsibility for these things must ultimately fall to humanity, and Hopebot is a means to empower that will to change, to heal, to help; to rise, continue, be.

Hopebot is always as big as it needs to be, even if it has to bring light to the entire world.

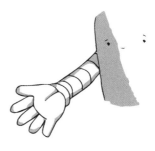

It starts with rising. Here, let Hopebot help.

HUGBOT

Requestbot: This robot is based on a suggestion by Twitter user @alienpmk

Primary Function:
Hugbot is the robot that gives you hugs, or offers hugs to others you send it to (but never touches without explicit consent).

Notable Features:
Pleasingly pliable surface, automatic propeller cut-out function, very slightly warm.

Dimensions:
Arm span sufficient to deliver a hug to anyone who wants one.

Sometimes you need a nice hug when there's no one around to give you one. Hugbot is just what you need to make you feel better. It gives nice, gentle embraces, but only to those who really need them – it's not just some obedient hugging machine! In fact, Hugbots aren't individually owned, but instead roam the skies, searching for those who need them, delivering their cheerful bounty. They don't interject themselves into serious situations – Hugbots don't descend en masse upon natural disasters or turn up at funerals or anything – but they're there, waiting, when you're ready.

Its propeller stops automatically when Hugbot initiates hugging protocols. This feature was introduced after initial prototypes delivered less-than-optimal hugs during test cuddles.

A whole kindness of Hugbots ascends to seek out their next targets, somewhere in the world.

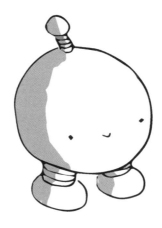

MONDAYBOT

Primary Function:
If you're feeling a bit glum on a Monday morning, Mondaybot will drop by to keep you company and just generally cheer you up by being a small round pal.

Notable Features:
Calendar application, good at hiding, very round.

Dimensions:
Pleasingly spherical.

Monday, in this modern world of ours, is its own source of anxiety. Whether it's the soul-destroying banality of a day job that provides only a subsistence lifestyle, the beginning of another news cycle with all its fresh horrors, or – worst of all – *school*, Monday mornings are their own special kind of hell. Mondaybot is the small ball of relief on the outside to combat the small ball of dread on the inside. It doesn't do anything – just turns up unerringly to potter around the house with you and be your friend. It'll distract you from what's to come, giving you the breathing space to get yourself ready and be out of the door on time. Monday won't go anywhere, but at least you'll always have Mondaybot.

Where does Mondaybot go Tuesday through Sunday? No one knows, but it always pops out when the time is right!

Don't read the news, not right now – talk to Mondaybot instead!

MONDAYBOT CROCHET PATTERN

By Sarah Penfold

Written in UK crochet terms. I haven't given gauge, but the material needs to be firm so stuffing doesn't show through. This could easily be scaled up or down by using different-weight yarn. Just make sure the stitches are tight together.

Materials
- DK weight yarn in a reassuring colour of your choosing
- 4mm crochet hook
- toy stuffing
- black yarn for sewing eyes/mouth (or 5mm safety eyes)
- tapestry needle

Body

Row 1: Using magic loop, work 6 stitches in a ring
Row 2: DC2 into every stitch (12 stitches)
Row 3: (DC2 into next stitch, DC1) six times (18 stitches)
Row 4: (DC2 into next stitch, DC2) six times (24 stitches)

Row 5: (DC2 into next stitch, DC3) six times (30 stitches)
Row 6: (DC2 into next stitch, DC4) six times (36 stitches)
Row 7: (DC2 into next stitch, DC5) six times (42 stitches)
Row 8: (DC2 into next stitch, DC6) six times (48 stitches)
Row 9: (DC2 into next stitch, DC7) six times (54 stitches)
Row 10: (DC2 into next stitch, DC8) six times (60 stitches)
Row 11–20: DC into every stitch

Place eyes between 15th and 16th round, leaving 8 stitches between them, and sew a mouth with black cotton 1 row below in-between the eyes.

Row 21: (DC2tog, DC8) six times (54 stitches)
Row 22: (DC2tog, DC7) six times (48 stitches)
Row 23: (DC2tog, DC6) six times (42 stitches)
Row 24: (DC2tog, DC5) six times (36 stitches)
Row 25: (DC2tog, DC4) six times (30 stitches)
Row 26: (DC2tog, DC3) six times (24 stitches)

I started stuffing here before it got too small, but stuff however you do. Make sure you stuff it tightly to hold shape.

Row 27: (DC2tog, DC2) six times (18 stitches)
Row 28: (DC2tog, DC1) six times (12 stitches)
Row 29: (DC2tog) six times (6 stitches)

Fasten off, leaving a long tail, then weave the tail in and out of last stitches and pull closed. Finish.

Antenna

Row 1: Using magic loop, work 6 stitches in a ring
Row 2: DC2 into every stitch (12 stitches)
Row 3–4: DC into every stitch
Row 5: DC2tog every stitch (6 stitches)

Stuff round bit of antenna

Row 6–10: DC into every stitch (6 stitches)

Leave long tail in order to attach to the top of the body.

Feet, make 2

Row 1: Using magic loop, work 6 stitches in a ring
Row 2: DC2 into every stitch (12 stitches)
Row 3: (DC2 into next stitch, DC1) six times (18 stitches)
Row 4: (DC2 into next stitch, DC2) six times (24 stitches)
Row 5: Working through the back loops only, DC every stitch
Row 6–7: DC into every stitch (24 stitches)
Row 8: DC2tog every stitch (12 stitches)
Row 9–11: DC into every stitch (12 stitches)

Fasten off, leaving a tail, and stuff the feet. Place feet on bottom of the body, evenly spaced so it can stand up, and sew on.

COMPANYBOT

Primary Function:
Companybot keeps you company.

Notable Features:
Telescopic legs, locating antenna, pretty easy-going.

Dimensions:
Average.

Companybot doesn't really do much. It doesn't tell jokes, it can't bring you drinks, it can't even throw a ball (no arms). But what it does excel at is being a good little robot pal and staying nearby to keep you company if you're lonely or sad or just need someone about the place. If you just want to hang out and watch TV, that's absolutely fine. Maybe go to the zoo? Sure – it likes tortoises, so make sure there's a good reptile house. How about a picnic? Companybot doesn't eat, but it likes sitting on tartan blankets and is fascinated by hampers. Whatever you need, Companybot is there for you.

What are you doing now? This doesn't look much fun!

Companybot also likes hide-and-seek, although admittedly it's better at the seeking part…

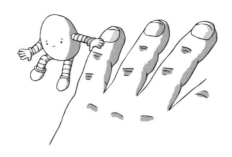

THEREBOT

(Content Warning: this robot's function is related to self-harm)

*Requestbot: This robot is based on a suggestion by Twitter user @blauerSchlumpf_*

Primary Function:
Therebot is there for you at all times, helping you to not self-harm. Holds your hand close to distract you. Soothes you with smiles. Listens and understands. Never judges.

Notable Features:
Unfaltering kindness, unending patience, unwavering support.

Dimensions:
Only small.

Some Small Robots are more serious than others. This is one of the most serious. If you suffer from a compulsion to harm yourself, Therebot is just a very small friend that is present in your life when you need it most. It doesn't do much, except be there. Sometimes that's enough.

Keep Therebot on your keys! A portable pal.

Even in the darkness, Therebot is close by.

BOTBOTS

Metabot
Conflictbot
Fixbot

It was inevitable that once the number of Small Robots grew large enough, there'd need to be some to corral the others into some sort of order. These are the Botbots: the Small Robots that assist with other Small Robots. I've left these ones till near the end because they don't make a lot of sense on their own – you sort of need to already know the deal with Small Robots to understand why these ones are necessary.

Some people have grown very attached to certain Small Robots. It's a source of fascination to me when they ask questions about them. As the one drawing them, I obviously have a certain authority when it comes to their capabilities, origins and so forth. But they're still just drawings, and no answers I can give will materially alter anyone's circumstances. Why does it matter if a fictional robot can do one thing but not the other? But, as much as this baffles me, I've begun to understand that fans of what I'm doing unquestioningly buy into the premise. Perhaps it's another of those human context-dependent things: we instinctively follow a narrative to its conclusion, without stopping to examine its real-world logic.

METABOT

Primary Function:
Have a problem? Not sure which Small Robot can solve it for you?
Consult Metabot! The 'bot that brings you 'bots!

Notable Features:
Full access to the Small Robots catalogue, knows the abilities and
limitations of all its fellow Small Robots, intuitive interface.

Dimensions:
Small, given its vast store of knowledge.

There are one hundred robots in this book alone, and there are many more in the back catalogue. It can be frustrating for people who are newcomers to our product range to try to find the robot they want. Because our solution is always a new robot, we invented Metabot, which can signpost you towards whatever other robot you need. Just approach Metabot with your request and it will instantly give you the name of your small, autonomous saviour and, if it's around, usher it into action.

People kept asking for Bigbot and unfortunately Metabot is powerless to distinguish between a sensible request and an idle longing for a big, stompy pal.

CONFLICTBOT

Primary Function:
Conflictbot negotiates conflicts between other Small Robots
whose functions are mutually exclusive.

Notable Features:
Calm demeanour, adaptive logic circuits, excellent listening protocols.

Dimensions:
Big enough to wade in and calm things down if needs be.

As the number and diversity of Small Robots began to proliferate, it became clear that certain conflicts were arising between them. One solution was to simply provide information about which robots weren't compatible with one another, but with so many robots being developed all the time, these errata would have grown swiftly unmanageable. A more dynamic solution was required, and that was Conflictbot. With a Conflictbot on hand, any time you have two Small Robots who want to carry out contradictory tasks, it can get them together to work it out. It's not always easy – Small Robots are nothing if not single-minded – but eventually harmony will be restored.

The sessions with Sleepbot and Loudbot were particularly trying, as every time Sleepbot spoke, Conflictbot fell asleep, only to be rudely awakened by Loudbot's booming voice.

FIXBOT

Primary Function:
Fixbot repairs other Small Robots that have been damaged.

Notable Features:
Full diagnostic suite, well-equipped toolbox, excellent benchside manner.

Dimensions:
Small enough to perform the most delicate precision engineering;
strong enough to heave open the heaviest access panel.

While all Small Robots are designed to be hard-wearing and incorporate numerous safety features to allow them to complete their programmed tasks, it's sadly inevitable that some will get damaged during the course of events. Initially, all robots requiring repairs had to be shipped back to our factory, but this was both inconvenient and not cost-efficient, so we solved the problem the way we solve all our problems: inventing a new robot. Fixbot can make any Small Robot as good as new. It's constantly updating its files via satellite link-up to HQ so that it's familiar with every single model in the catalogue. Whatever the issue with your Small Robot, Fixbot can repair it quickly and efficiently.

Fixbot can even tackle problems with robots' internal components.

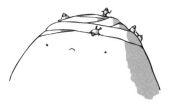

For bigger jobs, several Fixbots can work together to make repairs.

USELESSBOTS

Listen, not all Small Robots can be helpful. Some of them go a bit wrong in the production process, and some of them are just a bit… strange. Ironically, these robots are some of the best loved in the whole project. Or perhaps it's not that ironic – everyone loves an underdog, and what could be more sympathetic than a member of a cohort of automatons designed for specific purposes that have no purpose?

In fact, some fans have objected to the idea of 'Uselessbots', as if I'm insulting the Small Robots in this section. Sometimes they even try to suggest uses for them, as if calling them useless is a challenge. When people do this, I just reiterate that Uselessbots are useless and they were each created for a purpose – albeit a particularly obtuse one. Don't feel bad for them. A Small Robot is satisfied as long as it's doing what it was designed for, even if that's just being what it is.

FRIENDBOTS

Primary Function:
Friendbots keep each other company.

Notable Features:
Extendable limbs, mutual locator antennae, adorable.

Dimensions:
So small.

These robots were each invented to keep the other company. Why make two? Well, if we made one, it'd be lonely, wouldn't it? If we made three, one would be left out. Two is the perfect number, you see. Friendbots are inseparable, which is why they have stretchy arms – if one strays too far, the other can keep hold of it to make sure it comes back soon. Thankfully they don't often do that of their own volition, because Friendbots know they belong together.

Oh no!

A lone Friendbot: the saddest thing.

Phew! Reunited!

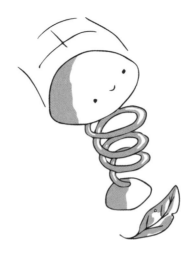

CRUNCHBOT

Primary Function:
Crunchbot crunches leaves in the autumn.

Notable Features:
High-tension spring locomotor, high-impact doofer, high-enthusiasm attitude.

Dimensions:
Big enough to crunch most domestic leaves.

Crunchbot is a classic example of Small Robots philosophy. Its task is to crunch leaves in autumn. Does it crunch anything else? No, just leaves. Does it crunch leaves in other seasons? What do you think? You might think you don't have a place in your life for Crunchbot, and you'd probably be right, but what *is* life without whimsy? Crunchbot is your springy, crunchy friend, and that might just be enough.

Yay! It's autumn at last!

Too many leaves.

UNICORNBOT

Requestbot: This robot is based on a suggestion by Twitter user @ayymanduh

Primary Function:
Unicornbot is a unicorn for some reason.

Notable Features:
Wonderful tail, important horn, small blep, insatiable curiosity.

Dimensions:
2.3 hands tall.

Unicornbot is not a very helpful Small Robot, but it is surely one of the best loved. It canters around the place, investigating anything it can find, normally using its tongue, which is where most of its sensory equipment is located. Its horn is potentially dangerous so it's recommended that, if purchasing a Unicornbot for a child, you put the small rubber cork provided onto the tip. It doesn't mind this too much, but it likes to do some digging with it now and then so try to give it at least an hour a day uncorked. When digging in this way, Unicornbot will produce small conical holes in which it stores anything it finds that it deems valuable, such as coloured paper or interesting buttons.

Unicornbot is a highly gregarious Small Robot, willing to make friends with almost anything. Keep an eye on your Unicornbot in case its trusting nature leads it into peril!

Herds of Unicornbots canter around the calibration meadows at Small Robots HQ, occasionally having small jousting contests to determine pecking order.

BOBBOT

Primary Function:
Bobbot is a floating round pal, able to be put to many uses, but mostly it's for going bob-bob-bob up and down.

Notable Features:
Geolocating antenna, buoyant construction, so round.

Dimensions:
Its mass divided by its volume is less than that of water.

What could be better than a little floaty friend? Bobbot fulfils this rather dubious need, bobbing up and down in the water. Maybe you could use it as a buoy for a boat, or for demarcating areas of the sea that are safe to swim in? Either way, Bobbot is happy. Perhaps the most famous use of this particular robot was when a flotilla was deployed by the Dorset Coastguard to guide a lost humpback whale out of Swanage Bay. The whale – dubbed Holly by locals – had followed a rogue Bigbot to shore, mistaking it for a member of its pod. Thankfully, the Bobbots were able to corral the confused cetacean back out to deeper waters, where it resumed its long migration.

How Bobbot floats

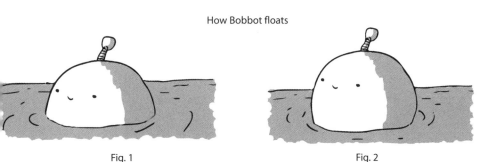

Fig. 1   Fig. 2

Flotilla of Bobbots to the rescue.

GHOSTBOT

Primary Function:
If you're worried your house may be haunted, deploy this spooky pal to patrol the area.

Notable Features:
Billowing skirt, silent hover unit, spooky as heck.

Dimensions:
Ephemeral.

No one wants to live in a haunted house but, to be fair, the ghosts were presumably there before you were. Rather than call in an exorcist or other form of spectral pest control, try Ghostbot to manage the problem in a humane (post-humane?) way. Ghostbot befriends any lurking poltergeists, wraiths, wights or will-o'-the-wisps it finds, ensuring you get a good night's sleep. During trials of Ghosbot units, all the volunteers surveyed reported complete satisfaction with its performance – not a single one of them was disturbed by a revenant spirit from beyond the grave! Hooray!

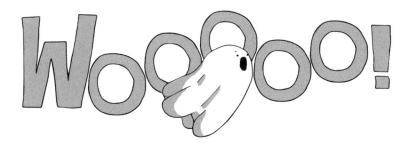

Look how spooky it is!

MISCHIEFBOTS

Primary Function:
Mischief.

Notable Features:
Chaos, anarchy, ruin, mess.

Dimensions:
Worry about the quantity, not the quality.

Hey, what's in this box? Oh it's some litt—
oh no! Oh there's hundreds of them! They're
out of control! Someone help! Nooooo!
They're in the petunias! They're making a
horrible mess
by the birdbath! They're ruining Mrs Deakin's
lovely spread! They've got Scotch egg
on the vicar's wife! Oh no, there's quiche
trodden into the marquee carpet! The
punch bowl is wobbling perilously close to
the prize certificates! Get out of there, you
horrid robots! They've pushed the mayor in

No! Leave Cakebot alone, you beastly creatures!

the duck pond! The mayor! They've trodden little footprints all over Mr MacTavish's prize
marrow! They've upset the verger! They've spilled ginger beer on the sausage rolls!

Oh no! We thought they'd gone but then they came back and they've been jumping in puddles and
now they have muddy feet and they're clambering all over the nice gingham tablecloths!

RECURSIVEBOT

Primary Function:
Due to a bizarre laboratory accident, Recursivebot is sitting on its own head.

Notable Features:
It's sitting on its own head. That's about it.

Dimensions:
That's… a complicated question.

Noooo! Why did
we make these?!

Someone at the Small Robots Development Lab had the bright idea to use the pocket universe within Storagebot to attempt to invent a method of faster-than-light propulsion. Something to do with creating a bubble of isolated space-time which could itself be shifted at superluminal velocity and therefore not violate causality. Anyway, this bright spark didn't do their sums right or something, because the aperture to the pocket universe ended up being inverted and now we've got a Small Robot that is sitting on its own head. Pretty annoying.

We asked Binsbot to try to explain what the hell happened, but it could only really hazard an educated guess.

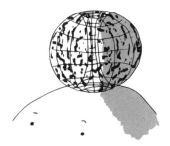

Finally we chanced upon a possible fix, by inverting the aperture back to its original configuration. Unfortunately, the nature of higher-dimensional space-time meant that the transform was incomplete and now the whole universe is on Recursivebot's head. Uh. Whoops.

BIGBOT

Primary Function:
Bigbot is just too big.

Notable Features:
Immense size.

Dimensions:
Too big.

Bigbot is simply much, much too big. Look at it. It's massive. A big gormless egg-shaped robot getting in the way and scaring innocent holidaymakers on the beach as it wades ashore. Some might say that, because Bigbot is self-evidently not small and clearly not remotely helpful, it made no sense for the Small Robots scientists to design it in the first place. Well, hindsight is twenty-twenty. Bigbot's here now, and it's not going anywhere – at least, not unless it wants to, because there's not much anyone can do to stop it once it gets moving. It doesn't even have arms, so it's not like it could reach for things either. It could knock things over if you needed them knocking over but, again, you'd have to point it in the right direction first and that's easier said than done. It won't even fit in your house. It's just too big, and that's all there is to it.

'Hello.'

A Note on the Author

Thomas Heasman-Hunt runs the popular Twitter account, Small Robots, which he launched in November 2017. His debut sci-fi novel, *Legacy*, was published by Cynefin Road in 2017.

@smolrobots

Acknowledgements

First of all, I'd like to thank my wife, Emma, whose unwavering support in this and all things is literally the only reason I bother to do much of anything. Not only were her mechanical woes the original source of the Small Robots concept, but the mutual aesthetic developed by the Heasman-Hunts over their years of association has informed everything about it since. So thanks, boo.

Thanks also to my parents: Mum, Dad, Keith and much missed Carol, all of whom have supported me in various ways over the years. Explaining this project to them was met with universal bafflement and I doubt it makes much more sense even now.

To the people at Unbound, thank you for taking a chance on this project, essentially apropos of nothing. I always hoped the Twitter account would reach the point that it might see print, but it happened faster than I expected and I'm still a bit confused about why. Nonetheless, they believed in me and the Small Robots and dutifully edited us all into some sort of coherence, for which I am of course absurdly grateful.

To my former colleagues in the day job I left behind to dedicate myself fully to what is, let's face it, not really a job in any meaningful sense, thank you for your patience as I tried (unsuccessfully) to juggle both sides of my life. They claim I'm missed, but I have my doubts.

Finally, the lion's share of my gratitude must go to the Small Robots family. The (at the time of writing) 8,580 people who have opted to follow the @smolrobots account on Twitter have almost without fail provided a constant source of support and inspiration and were also directly responsible both for lobbying Unbound to give this book a chance and then promptly funding it in an embarrassingly short time. They have latched onto this concept – and to me personally – with far greater enthusiasm than I deserve, and its runaway popularity is due to their word-of-mouth endorsements, not any kind of marketing skill on my part. I hope you all enjoy this distillation of the (again, at the time of writing) 820-ish robots that I have variously gifted to or inflicted upon you over the past couple of years.

If I forgot to thank you and should have, please assume simple negligence on my part. Any factual errors are, as always, the sole responsibility of the author.

Thomas Heasman-Hunt

PLEDGEBOTS

Not every robot is suitable for mass-production. Some are so specific, so personal, so weird, that only a prototype is ever made. Such are the Pledgebots shown here. Someone asked, we built; but everyone involved has agreed that things should end there. Let us say no more about these bizarre experiments in robot design.

ANDYBOT

A big joyful, sexy bearbot.

JENBOT

Stripy programming robot.

BANJOBOT

Folk-singing, banjo-playing round friend.

EXTRUDERBOT

A 3D printing pen robot. Gets upset if you try to take its hat off.

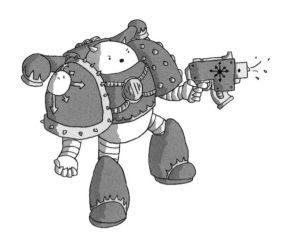

CHLOEBOT

A power-armoured robot dedicated to destroying the False Emperor with her water pistol.

MOUNTAINBOT

Determined to get to the top!

N0RMBOT

Likes to run (and run, and run…)

auuVBOT

Hapless little robot, always getting into scrapes.

SAZBOT

A robot of many hobbies, including playing recorder.

Unbound is the world's first crowdfunding publisher, established in 2011.

We believe that wonderful things can happen when you clear a path for people who share a passion. That's why we've built a platform that brings together readers and authors to crowdfund books they believe in – and give fresh ideas that don't fit the traditional mould the chance they deserve.

This book is in your hands because readers made it possible. Everyone who pledged their support is listed below. Join them by visiting unbound.com and supporting a book today.

Matthew Abbott
Caitlin Adams
Rob Agar
Carlo Albino
Alexis "Protomagicalgirl"
Moose Allain
Chloe Alsop
Erin Anderson
John Anderson
Melody Anderson
Cayden Andrews
Tamsin Andrews
K S Antoniw
Leanne Archbold
Gillian Armstrong
Phil Armstrong

Wendy Armstrong
Harriet Aspinall
Richard Attew
David Aument
auuV
Nicholas Avenell
Louise Ayling
Cathryn B
Richard Bairwell
Maxie Ballard
Berj & Laura Bannayan
Paul Barley
Bill Barnett
Adam D. Barratt
Lucy Barratt
Ann Marie Barrett

Mark Barton
Susan Bastian
Sarah Batty
Adam Baxter
Adele Beeken
Linda Beesley
Katy Bell
Nicholas Benn
Nick Bentley
Katherine Bialek
Chris Biggs
Nettie Birch
Ian Bishop
Carolyn Black
Holly Blades
Eleanor Blair
Ian Blake
Nick Bloxham
Èlia Boladeras i Viñas
Mireia Boladeras i Viñas
boop dragon
Hazel Bowley
Peter & Vicky Bradley
Shawn Brady
Michael Breen
Alan Brookland
Jess Brooks
Harriet Brown
Ricky Buchanan
Chris Bullock
Paul Bulmer

Hann Bunn
Laura Burns
Marcus Butcher
Phil Byrne
Gwynne Callow
Vikki Campbell
Matteo Cancellieri
Captain Science
Christine Carlton
Alexander Carroll
Cathy Carroll
Sian Carstairs
Kerry Carter
Drew Castledine
Faith Caton
Chrissie Caulfield
Kim Cave-Ayland
Renée Chadwick
Rohan Chadwick
Dan Chalmers
Alex Chiang
Rachel Chilton
Christina Christidou
A Clark
Caroline Clark
David Clarke
Jill Clarke
Hanna & Anna Clutterbuck-Cook
Helen Coates
Geoffrey Cochran
Richard Cohen

Rachel Coleman
Toast Conger
Emma Conkling
John Conley
Ciaran Conliffe
Kirsty Connell-Skinner
Helen Connor
Emma Copson
Sarah Cornell
Brian Corteil
Damien Cross
Liz Curry
Matty Curry
Maria Cygan
Karen Dale
Susannah Darby
Patricia Dark
David, Holly and Kit
Ian Davies
Nicola Davies
Steph Davies
Vic Davies
Melissa Davies & Phil Tickner
Gary Davis
Janet Davis
Indira Day
Sarah Devonshire
Emmy Dickens
Miranda Dickinson
Roz Dixon-Burnett
Andy Donaldson

Darla Donna
Peter Dray
Kingfisher Drew
Sandy Driskell
Katy Driver
Esther Dudek
Michael Dunn
Nick Dunn
Alexander S. Dutton
Bethan E
Chris Eagle
James Eagle
Alison Edwards
Sheila Edwards
Tom Elcock
Laura Ellen
Rebecca Elliot
Emily, Jon and Axl Owen
Lewis English
Kate Evans
Paul Evans
Chloe Everei
Kiera Exley
Dan Fairs
Avory Faucette
Claire Faulkner
Kate Faulkner
Felltir
Deborah Fern
Patric ffrench Devitt
Andrea Fidgett

Shona Fidgett

Mark Fine

Samantha Finnigan

Tanya Fish

Alexander Fleming

Joanna Forbes

Rachael Fox

D Franklin

Ruth Franklin

Ben Fritzson

@futureidentity

Sarah G

Leila Gabasova

Neelam Gandevia

Heather Gaona

Silph Gemini

Steve Gennard

Sally Gibson

Giles

Richard Gillin

Carlin Gilroy

Mark Giltrow

Hayden Glass

Kate Armageddon Glover

Tara Glover

Eleanor Goldsmith

Dr Janet Goodall

Helen Gordon

Saira Gorringe

Inez Gowsell

Kristian Grapes

greatbig lizard

Joshua Green

Simon Greenwood

Clare Griffiths

Paul Griffiths

Gromit, c/o Samantha Smith

Maria Angela Guzman

H

Nina Haerland

Halo Café Celbridge

Jordan Han

Thomas Hanke

Gillian Hardy

Julie Hardy

Tim & Ros Hardy

Emily Harford

Kate Harford

Penny Harper

Becca Harper-Day

Simon Harris

Alison Hawke

Stevy Haworth

Julian Hazeldine

Erwin Heemsbergen

Katherine Hegarty

Vicky Hempstead

Kelly Henley

Rosemary Herbert

Adrian Hickford

Alison Hindenlang

Joshua Hochstetler

Heather Hodge
Ann Hodgson
Simon Holden
George Holt
Anna Hopkins
Michael Horne
Katherine Hougham
Jon Hudson
Miles Hudson
Emma Humphries
Brian Hunt
Lucy Hunt
Dave Hutchinson
Harriet Hutchinson
Kay Hutt
Ben Hutton
Ittai
Sarah Jackson
Anna James
Lee Jaschok
Ben Jemmett
Jen
Laura Jennings
Callum Jessamine
Brendan Johnson
Colin Johnson
Zoe Johnson
Dylan Jones
Frances Jones
Jennifer Jones
Rebecca Jones

Rob Jones
Rori Jones
Sarah Jones
Sharon Jones
Julie Kangas
Kamla Kasichainula
Katy
Adam Kay
Georgie Kay
Ben Kehoe
Anna Kessling
Dr Mohsin Khan
Dan Kieran
Jenn King Sallee
Justin Kinney
Caroline Kirk
Sarah Kirkland
Lukas Daniel Klausner
Gareth Klose
Irene Knapp
Alison Knight
Julie Knight
Marie-Anne Knight
Paul Knox-Kennedy
William Knox-Walker
Simon Koppel
Martin Kunert
Karen Lake
Thomas Lake
Resa LaMont
Patricia Larash

Lars
H Latham
Alex Lee
Jacqueline Lee
Patty Lee
Matthias Lehner
Ella Mae Lewis
Carol Lewis Powell
Richard Leyton
Matteo Licata
Lidbert
Ruby Lilith
Helen Lippell
ATM Livesey
Gwyneth Lockwood
Amanda Lusky
Terri MacDonald
Michael Maclean
Mike MacMartin
Alex Mallinson
Karanasou Maria
Hannah Martin
Jenny Martin
Elli Masson
Barbara Mattson
Florian Maushart
Mauve
Sarah Mayman
Elizabeth McClellan
Tara McCook
Jon McCorkell

Clair McCowlen
Chris McDermott
SarahLouise McDonald
Grainne McEntee
Sharon McGuinness
Anne McHenry
Emma, Paul & Sam McKenzie
Nuala McKernan
Kathryn McNeil
Simon Meadows
Ivenne Mecking
Ellen Mellor
Nigel Metheringham
Veerle Metten
Deborah Metters
Mikayla Micomonaco
Jonathan Miles
Brian Milton
Christian Misterovich
Cyndee Mitchell
John Mitchinson
James Moar
G Molloy
Wren Montgomery
Drake Moore
Dee Morgan
Kole Morgan
Sarah Morriss
Jules Murden-Brown
Brett Myers
Justin Myers

Carlo Navato
Will Needham
Rosie Newton
Fiona Nielsen
Colin Nocetti
Stewart Nolan
Jay Nolde
Norm
Chris Novus
Sue Nowakowski
Fiona Nowling
Dervla O'Brien
Alex O'Donnell
Sophie O'Reilly
Ciara O'Sullivan
Karen O'Sullivan
Alan Outten
Bill Owens
Victoria Oxberry
Katherine Pace
Nathan Pace
Tom Panton
Steven Pape
Julia Parascandolo
Lev Parikian
Victoria Parkinson
Jo Hanna Pearce
Louise Penn
Jason Peper
Bob Phillips
Debbie Phillips

Liz Philpots
CJ Picklesimer
Laura Pilling
Thyreast Pinckney
Ian Pinsker
Justin Pollard
Jon Poole
Anthony Pratt
Lawrence Pretty
Kate Prior
Alec Proffitt
Joseph Provo
Daria Pydorenko
David Pye
Emma Quigley
Ryan Quinlan
Nicky Quint
Isaac R-G
Erika Raffle-Currie
Craig Rathbone
Levi Rayka
Nora Reed
Bethan Rees
Registrar Trek
The Reids
Andrew Rendle
Gill Rennie
Neil Reynolds
Sioned-Mair Richards
Tim Richardson
Juliet Roberts

Emily D. Robertson

Katharine Robertson

The robots from Nothing

Charlie Rodgers

Lisa Roels

Lucy Rogers (@DrLucyRogers)

Nick Rolfe

Tim Rouse

Matthew Rowell

Catherine Rowlands

Liz Russ

Stef S

S B

Ben Scarboro

Chris Scarr

Burkhard Schafer

Griffin Schnitzler

Diane Schultz

SpookyTreasonHunter Heather Schwartz

Sarah Scotcher

Fiona Scott

Joseph Seager

Kirsty Sedgman

Katherine Series

Emma Sewell

Jacob Sewell

Grace Seybold

Linda Shacklock

Abbi Shaw

Isobel Sheene

Marion Jane Sheffield

Mike Sheldon

Jo Short

Bevan Shortridge

Barbara Simmons

Seumas Skinner

Courtney Slater

@SmallRabbit

Emma Smith

James Smith

Martin Smith

Samantha Smith

Geoff Snowman

Gert Sønderby

Julie Sorrell

Maureen Kincaid Speller

Spike

Tabatha Stirling

Beth Stites

Natasha Stone

Katie Stowell

Claudia Strauss

Ilona Stretch

Rebecca Strickland

Beth Stuart

Caroline Stupnicka

Erin Subramanian

Archer Sully

Nida Yasin Suri

Giles Sutcliffe

Kat Swindells Ridley

Margaret Taylor

Paul Taylor
Angharad Thomas-Richards
Unnar Thor Thorisson
Elisabeth Thornton
Jen Thornton
Paul Tildsley
Emma Tilston
Monica Toth
Robin Triggs
Helen Tucker
TwoTone and all our llamas sadly lost
Amandeep Uppal
Dan Vail
Kassandra Velez
Milo Vermeulen
Caroline Viac
Joyclyn Vincent
Andrew Waddie
Marion Wahlberg
Simon Waldman
Dominic Walker
E Walker
Lorna Walker
Corey Wallis
Mike Wallis
A Walter
Nikki Walters
Matt Warburton
Charlie Warren
Dawn Wedge
Rose Weedon

Chris Weixelman
Peter Wells
Clair Wellsbury-Nye
Matthias Werner
Hannah Whelan
Elizabeth White
Tom Whitlock
Rob Whitnell
Hayley Wickens
Charlotte Wightwick
Jack Wilhelm
Rhys Wilkins
Emma Wilkinson
David Williams
Lindsay Williams
Catherine Williamson
Kirsty Willis
Samantha Willis-Hall
Aaron Wilson
Magdalen Wind-Mozley Rosewind
Jonathan Windeatt
Katy Windeatt
Seren Wood
Laura Woods
Kate Woolfitt
Eleanor Wort
Liz Wray
Jordan Wright
Emma Wright (editorialgirl)